100 Days

100 Days

How I saved my life
and can help transform yours

Hannah Sturland

Published by Fuzzy Flamingo
www.fuzzyflamingo.co.uk

ISBN 978-1-8380944-9-2

Important Note
This book is not intended as a substitute for medical advice or
treatment. Any person with a condition requiring medical attention
should consult a qualified medical practitioner or suitable therapist.

A CIP catalogue record for this book is available from the British
Library

Cover and Typesetting: Jen Parker, Fuzzy Flamingo
www.fuzzyflamingo.co.uk

One Day or Day One. You Decide

Contents

Introduction

It started as a gradual slide, an erosion of my ability to live, so gentle that I couldn't see it coming until one day it hit me: I don't want to live anymore.

I have a fantastic life; a husband, two gorgeous children, a successful career and a lovely house. But what people don't see – because I never let them – is the overwhelming, crippling anxiety that dominates my life.

I work in the public sector as a project manager, directing teams of people to deliver multi-million-pound projects. My children go to the village school where I am an active member of the PTFA. Our house is large and well-kept with home-cooked meals regularly on the table. I work hard at appearing as if I have it all. Yet there are times when my anxiety is so bad I can't leave the house, where I cancel plans with my closest friends because I can't bear to be around other people for fear of being found out.

I have spent my life devising coping mechanisms and avoidance strategies. I know what's 'safe' and what's so unknown that I can't risk it for fear of a panic trigger, or worse. Each day is a carefully constructed routine of 'safe' activities and within this routine I am a confident, capable, successful human.

And so it was that a series of seemingly small, unrelated incidents brought my world crashing down around me.

Things were great at work; I was loving my exciting new project and had the freedom to use my creativity to deliver in new ways. I was especially pleased because after years of issues since having children I'd been referred to a dietician for IBS support. I could finally see the light at the end of a long, frustrating tunnel and I was keen to get started, sure I could handle any dietary changes, even though I'd always found it tough on my anxiety before.

It turns out that the intense focus on everything I was putting into my body was more than I could handle. I began to skip meals because I couldn't face the ordeal of preparing something that met with the strict restrictions of an elimination diet. I stuck to bland gluten-free toast and occasionally homemade soup until the thought of eating turned my stomach and I just stopped trying.

I was exhausted, under-nourished and my anxiety was taking over. I arranged to work from home, only going into the office for meetings so that I only had to keep up the 'I'm fine' act for short periods of time.

I went back to the dietician and begged to re-introduce my 'safe' foods in the hope that I'd be able to eat again. But I'd barely moved past toast when my youngest caught a sickness bug. My anxiety increased and I struggled with eating even more as I was convinced

I'd catch the bug. Then a week later my eldest caught it and I lost control.

Still, I was convinced that once he was better and I hadn't caught anything then I'd be fine again. I'd be able to start eating and recover my normal routine. So, I just kept working away, keeping the curtain of normality intact.

My anxiety continued to take over and I was struggling to handle the persistent thoughts and images that dominated my mind and prevented me sleeping. I knew this would seem ridiculous to anyone else, so I kept quiet and carried on pretending, breaking down in tears at every private opportunity because I felt so exhausted and utterly helpless.

I'd organised the Christmas fair for the PTFA and was on my way to set up, but I just couldn't stop crying. A friend asked if I was okay and I broke down sobbing, telling her I was stressed and hadn't been sleeping, but reassuring her that I was okay.

I knew that was a lie. I was far from okay.

I'd spent the last few weeks carefully weighing up the options for ending my life. I'd planned letters for my family and just needed the weather to get colder so that I could put my plan into action. This terrified me but I couldn't stop thinking about it. I continually asked my husband to stay home with me because I didn't feel safe. I was utterly broken, unable to even pretend to be my normal self anymore. I was terrified of the impact this was having on my children and convinced I'd lose my job and everything I cared about. I shut down; not sleeping, barely eating yet continuing to work from home, a trembling shadow of my former self.

After the Christmas fair, I reached out to my mum and told her how much I was struggling and that I couldn't get better by myself. She took me to the GP and we asked for help. The GP was lovely but offered very little help, although I am on a waiting list! I have had to fight every day to stay alive and find my way to live again. Throughout my journey I wrote a daily journal, sharing my thoughts, feelings and experiences, which helped me to find a way to recovery that's meant I have built a new life for myself. A life that is happy, authentically me and one which is helping me sustain my recovery and improve my mental health.

In this book I share with you my journal entries and the method I used to build my recovery, to bring you my reality and show you that no matter what, you are not alone. There's no glossing over the rawness, nothing to make it prettier or less bleak. I'm not a trained mental health expert, but I have lived this. I am an expert in my own experience and I'm sharing it here in the hope that it will help you too.

If you are struggling with your mental health or feel trapped in a life that causes stress, exhaustion or a feeling that there must be something more than this, then read on. Learn how to be your best self and find space between your waves by using simple, effective tools for achieving authentic, sustainable mental health. Mental health is different for everyone, but whether you've got a diagnosis from your GP, you don't feel able to seek formal support, or maybe you just want to make a change in your life – this book can help. There are loads of different tools out there, but it can be really overwhelming to try and find something that feels right and start using it. These tools and exercises are the ones I have used in my recovery and continue to use to keep myself well, and they're a great place to start taking those baby steps forward.

But first just sit, take a breath and another… really breathe deep into your belly and let your body relax. I know that you probably have a lot going on right now and often it feels like you might drown under the weight of pressure, expectation, or a chronic condition. But I know you can do this – you can take anything life throws at you because you are strong – hell you're fierce – and I know you can do it. I also know that sometimes you feel anything but fierce and you can't even find the strength to pull yourself out of bed in the morning. I can empathise with that, I've been there. So, stay in bed if you need to, call in sick, let the children watch television. It's okay.

You are not alone.

There's an army of us who know how you feel, and we all want to help. Breathe, just breathe and have a read of this book; take comfort from knowing you've got company and that however dark things get you can find the light again.

H x

Chapter 1

Crisis Point

I think it's only fair to give you a warning here: this first chapter is pretty emotional! If you are affected by anything you read please, please reach out and talk to someone, either a friend or family member or one of the organisations listed at the back of this book. Stick with it, though – it does get better!

Day 1

I'm broken. I truly feel that I've reached a key turning point in my life because I cannot carry on.

The way I see it I have three options: 1. end it all, 2. get well and carry on, or 3. get well and learn how to stay well.

I choose three.

I'm not going to lie, a week ago, a day ago even, I was ready to choose one. It'll be a battle for a while, things have become pretty bad (understatement of the year!), but I've asked for help and I'm learning to stand up for myself and say 'no' when I need to so I can try and get the help I need.

I want to understand my triggers for anxiety and

depression so I can build in guards against them. I want to learn to accept that this is who I am, that it's okay and that I can still be a good wife, mother, friend, human just as I am.

I want to do practical things like check hormone and mineral levels to understand what balance looks like for me. I want to understand how I can help myself to eat, sleep, rest and find peace as a regular part of living. I want to learn how to balance my ambition with needing to simplify and sometimes slow down.

There are so many things I want to do; enjoy my kids, help at their school, be successful at work, turn the charity I've just started into something that's delivering real change, spend time on my hobbies... but I know that all needs me to get well.

I just need to hang in there until my mental health assessment appointment in a week's time then hopefully we'll have the beginnings of a plan for my recovery. I know it'll be a long road, which won't always run smoothly, but I now have hope and the support of my family.

Here's to day one, may there be many more to come.

H x

Day 2

A day to breathe. The children were happy to explore their new toys for a while, so I was able to rest and just potter about. I took a quiet five minutes to open my Christmas presents from a friend, which are incredibly thoughtful and bring tears to my eyes as I feel the full weight of my guilt over the worry and sadness I'm causing those I love.

I go outside and take some deep breaths. I can't let this feeling overwhelm me or I might never resurface. That helps and the pain starts to recede as I notice the gorgeous sunny day and my breathing levels out.

I love being outside in this weather, so I stick on my gardening gloves and do a bit of clearing up and pruning. I'm taking it steady but manage to get quite a bit done in the half hour I'm out there. It feels good to achieve something.

I received a message from a friend who is visiting from abroad; we're all getting together for a cuppa and catch up later. It feels daunting to go out and connect with people: I don't want them to see how broken I am, and I certainly don't want to spoil the catch up for everyone. I know that I'll hate myself if I don't go and will use it as a stick to beat myself with for days. So, I have a really hot shower – always calming – and off I go.

It's lovely to see my friends. They are kind and offer support. We talk about Christmas, the children, work and house moves, and it's wonderful to feel connected again. I wish I could hold on to this feeling so that next time isn't so hard, but I know that's not the nature of anxiety.

I'm exhausted this evening and battling anxious thoughts as a result. "Things will get better" is my mantra at the moment, so I repeat it to myself whilst focusing on my breathing.

It's hard to have hope at times like this. Just got to keep breathing.

H x

Day 3

I'm struggling today. I'm exhausted despite everything my husband and family are doing to make things easier for me and I feel so frustrated at my inability to do anything useful.

I feel so angry at myself and have no headspace to approach things rationally. When will this end? Will I always have to fight this? I'm not sure I can do this.

I need to try and focus on something positive so that I don't fall into a hole. I'll write more later…

… A few hours spent in the garden and crafting have rescued the day. I'm thankful that my husband prompted me to take some time out because it's something I'm terrible at asking for but desperately need.

I wish there were instructions for mental illness so that I could understand 'why' and 'how' and 'what now', but I guess that's the point – it's different for everyone, so there are no easy answers.

I'm holding my breath for the mental health assessment appointment next week in the hope that there will be answers, a treatment plan and a way forward to feeling better. Maybe that's too much to hope for. But at least, right now, I have hope again.

I know now that hope is a key ingredient for me; it's when I lose hope that the darkness sets in and I'm not able to see my way through. That's when recovery feels impossible, like there is no way to carry on.

Trouble is, hope is precarious, especially when I'm not

well. Hope can disappear in an instant and take an age to resurface. Better hold on tight whilst I have it.

H x

Day 4

Today has been hard. We'd arranged for some family to visit and it's great to see them, but my anxiety was rocket-powered as a result.

I couldn't sit still this morning; beta blockers took the edge off the panic, but I couldn't shake the thoughts and feelings that something terrible was going to happen.

I kept myself busy with some gardening and then cleaning until everyone arrived. It was great to see everyone and the children played brilliantly together, but still I struggled to relax.

I must seem really grumpy and withdrawn but, honestly, it's just a battle to be sitting here breathing, so I can't do any more.

I wish it wasn't like this. I wish I could go out or have people over spontaneously without hours, heck sometimes days of feeling like I'm about to step off a cliff but don't know where the edge is.

I feel completely drained. I'm hiding upstairs because I need some time away from people – but this means I'm not playing games with my children and I feel so bloody awful for not being able to. What a crap mum I am.

It's bloody hard trying to pull myself out of this; always reminding myself to breathe, remembering to say reassuring things to myself so that my brain doesn't run away down a dark path. I'm not very good at it yet, not very good at being kind to myself, not very good at asking for the help I need. How on earth am I going to get better if I can't even do the simplest of things?

Still, the day is almost over and I'm still here, still breathing. That's going to have to be enough for today, sorry.

H x

Day 5

Things are bad. Very bad.

I can't sit still; I'm struggling to write. Just waiting for my mind to shut down completely.

I want to run, screaming, shouting so that someone, anyone, might hear and help me. But what's the point? No one can make it stop.

I can't do this. I have nothing left to fight with. I just want it all to stop.

Day 6

I feel pretty desolate this morning; apathetic, empty, bland. I've spent the night battling suicidal thoughts and just trying to stay safe.

I hate New Year's Eve – there's so much nonsense about improving yourself, achieving great things or changing your life for the New Year. What an absolute load of rubbish.

It's cold, often wet and pretty pants in January, and February too for that matter, so we'd be better off staying snug at home, taking it easy and celebrating all we achieved the previous year.

More than ever, I feel the pressure this year. Pressure to be well, to be able to cope with life again, pressure to do better.

I'm just so tired of feeling like this. The thought of spending a new year, a whole year, feeling like this is crushing me. I can't do that.

This NYE the only resolution I'm making is to fight. For myself, for whatever I need to get well, I will fight. When I feel like I can't fight anymore I will ask for help.

This year I will fight to survive.

H x

Day 7

I wake up to a day filled with expectation, promises and commitments but I feel nothing.

A complete absence of any feeling; I am numb.

It takes everything I've got to pull myself out of bed to face the day. A day that, for me, is like trying to use a fork to push treacle uphill.

I dreamt that the changing year would ease this feeling of isolation and hopelessness, but the stark reality hit me this morning.

It's the end of the holiday period; family return to other parts of the country, work, school and 'normal life' resume for the rest of us. Except I can't face it. The feeling of desolation washes over me throughout the day, never-ending like the tide.

I am terrified of what the next few days and weeks will bring. I can't go back to 'normal life', but I'm terrified to lose it. I've been surrounded by family who know the truth of what I'm feeling, and they've kept me going, supported me and the children, and I don't know what to do when that ends.

Just two more days until my mental health assessment appointment and I'm hoping, desperately, for some guidance, support and most of all hope. Hope that there is help out there, hope that we can make a plan for treatment, hope that I won't always feel like this.

I'm trying to prepare for the appointment so I make sure I give a full picture of what I'm feeling and my state of mind but it's nearly impossible when my brain is throwing things at me at a zillion miles an hour and the only thing I can do is scream.

Finally, it's time to crawl back into bed; my sanctuary from the world but also the place where I've no escape from my mind.

Still, at least I can cry here without upsetting anyone else.

H x

Day 8

Awful night; woke up in a state of complete panic multiple times, anxiety dreams, racing thoughts – the works.

So, I'm even more exhausted today; tearful, snappy, more tears. Plus, it is the day that our family Christmas officially ends because my sister goes home.

It's been so great having her here; extra support from someone I don't have to wear a mask for and reminders of who I am, outside of this illness. Although there's always something I'm holding back – I don't want to worry people more than I have to.

Now that's over and I need to try and get back to 'normal life' – food planning, shopping, cleaning, taking the children out and about. Trouble is, I don't feel remotely ready to face any of that. Maybe the mental health assessment appointment tomorrow will help me feel ready.

I did have a really good session with my solution-based therapist today. I accessed the employee assistance programme through work and found I can have six sessions with her. Today was session two and we talked more about how I'm feeling, how those feelings are manifesting and having an impact on my life and drawing inferences as to the connections between them.

It is really interesting and very emotional! But reflecting back now, what we talked about really resonates with me. I'm looking forward to the next session where we'll work on solutions for a particular area that I can then use as my place of respite – one good thing for when it all gets too much.

Now I need to have a quiet evening, convince myself to eat something and then hopefully get a good night's sleep so that I can handle the mental health assessment tomorrow.

H x

Day 9

I actually had a good night's sleep last night. It's so rare that I get to say that, but my mum made me a weighted blanket and it is awesome!

We're off to my mental health assessment today and I'm feeling really apprehensive. I'm desperate for some help but my anxiety means that I'm also catastrophising (to use a term I learnt in therapy) about what that help might be: will it be medication that numbs me, causes side effects or just does nothing? Will I be able to access therapy quickly or will it be months of waiting, of battling to survive just one more day?

The appointment was hard going, very emotional and now I'm utterly exhausted. But I felt listened to and supported, which really helps.

The outcome is medication (one I've not tried before) and a referral to the Community Mental Health Team for making a treatment plan. The first appointment will likely be in a couple of weeks, but I can pick up the medication tomorrow.

I'm hugely apprehensive about taking medication; I don't even like taking paracetamol for a headache! But the nurse said the meds will help get me into the right place for therapy and to be honest it feels like if I don't agree to take them, I won't get any other help.

I can't stop the anxious thoughts, but I know that I have the support of my husband and family so when tomorrow comes I'll take the tablet and see what happens. Hopefully it'll be okay and, if not, I know I can speak up and there'll be support for me to try something else.

For now, I'm looking forward to snuggling under my weighted blanket again, goodnight!

H x

Day 10

I'm feeling very much like I can't cope with life today. It all feels too much, and I just want to sink into oblivion.

I can't do that, though; the children want to play and there's laundry and cleaning to do. Actually, sod the cleaning, I really can't face that today.

I wish my brain would change the record – 'I can't do this' and 'they'd be better off without you' on and on until I want to scream. I don't know how to make it stop but I really wish I did.

I feel really vulnerable; incapable of looking after myself and not remotely able to function. I wonder if this feeling will ever leave, or will it just be louder at times and quieter at others? I know there's no cure, but I can't bear the thought that it'll always be like this.

I can't decide whether it's better for me to be around my family and have some semblance of normality or whether the best thing would be to go away, where I can just focus on surviving. This feels appealing but where would I go? Who would keep me safe when I'm not able to do it myself?

I picked up my medication today; hopefully that will help. As long as I can convince myself to take it and not let the anxious thoughts get the better of me.

I'm just so tired of being a burden. Why can't I pull

myself together, take the tablets and crack on with life?

I'm not sure I can get through any more days like this. But I know I've survived this far and if I can just hang in there more help is coming.

H x

Day 11

Wow. The label on my new medication has a warning for drowsiness but I didn't expect to be knocked out for eleven hours! Even when I 'woke up' this morning I couldn't open my eyes. It's taken me an hour and a half to be able to open my eyes properly and get out of bed. It's a scary feeling!

Now that I'm up I feel groggy and my brain is fuzzy, plus I feel quite shaky and unnerved by the inability to wake up. I'll have a drink and force some food down to see if that helps.

I'm trying to fill my day with positive things so that I don't sit and fret about the medication. I'm doing a bit of research for the Etsy shop and then I need to take down the Christmas decorations.

It does help to have something else to focus on for a while, but I have the concentration span of a bored toddler at the moment, so I need to have a list of tasks that I can rotate through. At least these tasks help me feel a small sense of achievement; I can't leave the house or function as an adult, but I can update the Etsy listings from the safety of the sofa! All progress is good, right?

The knowledge that my recovery sits squarely with

me is terrifying. I don't know that I've got what it takes to pull myself through this. Taking any positive steps feels overwhelming yet insignificant – like using a raindrop to change the tide – but I know that's what recovery is built on.

For now, I'm going to take the tiny step of taking my next tablet and going to bed earlier in the hope that I feel better tomorrow. It's the last day of the holidays and I'd like to be able to at least spend some time with the children before they go back to school. I'm trying not to think about going back to work...

H x

REST – the first step

In the early days of any mental health crisis or life-changing event, the focus really needs to be on rest: getting enough rest and the right kind of rest. Your body and mind are going through an awful lot, so try and sleep when you feel sleepy and rest when you need to.

If you're struggling to sleep there are lots of things you can try from cutting down on caffeine, getting some fresh air and gentle exercise to journaling and meditation. It can feel really overwhelming to try something new when you're utterly exhausted, so take it easy on yourself, give yourself space to listen to your inner voice and go with what feels right.

It's about more than sleep, although getting enough good quality sleep is essential for recovery and general well-being. Rest is about finding time and activities that help you find peace and respite throughout the day.

These activities will vary for each of us, but here's what works for me:

1. Safe Space: Finding a safe space to stop and meditate, collect my thoughts, gain control over my emotions or just read a book.

    For me, the rest comes in having a safe space where I can breathe deeply, calm my mind and body and spend a few minutes centring myself so that I feel able to face whatever comes next.

    My safe space is always somewhere I can be alone, and I've worked to identify safe spaces that aren't just at home so that I can tap into the benefits wherever I am. My car is a safe space, walking in the countryside or on a beach is a safe space, an empty office at work can be a safe space. Spaces where I can cry, rant or have a panic attack, spaces I know I can access and find the strength to face whatever comes next. It's about creating the conditions you need to be able to take a moment for yourself and find peace.

2. Distractions: I have a couple of favourite TV shows I watch, and I always have a book

or two on the go. I make jewellery and I like to write. These activities give my body the chance to be still, with the added benefit of stilling the chaos in my mind too. I often have trouble choosing something to do, to the point where I end up doing nothing or mindlessly scrolling social media, which isn't helpful for me. I started writing activities on scraps of paper and pulling them out of a jar. If I don't fancy the activity, I just pull another one out. This strategy really helped me make the most of rest time and I'm getting better at recognising what activity I need at any given time.

3. Go to bed: Sometimes there's no better solution. Have a nap, read a book, listen to a meditation or some music. Bed is my ultimate safe space.

Exercise

What makes you feel safe?

Next time you feel calm – whether that's a specific place or during an activity – make a note: when have your shoulders come down from around your ears? When has your breathing deepened, or your heart rate levelled out? Where do you get that 'ahhhhh' feeling of relief, relaxation and safety?

Use a journal or head to my website (https://www.thementalhealthcommunity.co.uk/tools)   to download a worksheet so you can make a note and refer back to it whenever you feel the need.

Chapter 2

Early Days

These early days are all about survival (my word of the year is SURVIVE) and trying to figure out how to get through it all and move forward, however slowly. It's easy to put pressure on yourself to do too much or be better than you feel, especially if you have people around you who are trying to help – it can feel like there's an expectation for you to bounce back. I know it's hard, but it's so important that you take things at your own pace and that you're kind to yourself.

The days covered in this chapter see the end of the Christmas holidays and returning to work and 'normality'. I felt huge pressure to be better than I actually felt (most of this pressure was from myself). I was also slowly learning that the external help I so desperately needed wasn't going to come anytime soon.

Day 12

I've woken up today feeling like I've actually had a half decent sleep and opening my eyes isn't a massive struggle – win!

I've got a bit more oomph today, so I managed to get some cleaning done. I love a clean house; it really does help my mind feel more peaceful if everywhere is clean and tidy. I know that sounds silly, but it's true.

Today is the last day of the holidays – back to school and work tomorrow. I think I'm struggling with it because it means the end of this calmer, family-filled bubble that's been getting me through the last couple of weeks. Now it's coming to an end and I still don't have any additional support or a treatment plan in place. The next week feels pretty daunting.

There's so much waiting – once I asked for help and admitted how bad things were, I hoped I'd get some help fairly quickly. But there are lots of assessments and people to keep telling your story to before decisions are made about what help is best.

I always worry that I've missed something out or that I'm not getting across just how desperate and hopeless I feel. I think the sad truth is that there are just many, many people who need help, and resources are very stretched.

I have at least one more assessment this week; occupational health at work. I'm not sure what might come out of it, but I'll tell my story again and see what happens.

Work… something that's often kept me going when other things get too much. I hope it can help pull me out of the darkness again. I guess we'll find out this week. Wish me luck!

H x

Day 13

Wow 7am was hard to face this morning! I'm not sure if it was the lack of sleep or the thought of getting the kids ready for school or facing my inbox... probably a combination of all three. In reality, the kids were great and went off to school with no problems. It's when I turned my laptop on that the fun really started.

I should qualify what I'm about to write by explaining that I do actually like my job – I work with some great people and I really believe in the work I'm doing. Plus, the organisation is being really supportive of my mental health wobble. But I was totally unprepared for the feeling of overwhelming panic that hit me when I logged in this morning.

It wasn't the volume of emails or anything particularly nasty to deal with but the weight of expectation – expectation that I'd be well now, that I'd be back in the office, that I'd be able to have a conversation about what a great Christmas I'd had.

But that's not how things are and the weight of that nearly broke me this morning.

I've had to talk myself through the day; staying focused on small tasks and taking regular breaks to do some breathing exercises. I've survived, though, and achieved some good things at work, which is something to be celebrated.

I've got nothing left now. I'm completely exhausted and can't even face making dinner or eating anything.

That's probably a sign that the balance isn't right at

the moment, but I can't think straight enough to work out what needs to shift. At least I made it through the day; maybe there'll be space for thinking tomorrow.

H x

Day 14

After yesterday I made a promise to myself that I wouldn't sit and stare at my laptop all day today. So, after a good morning's work I headed out into the garden for some fresh air and exercise in the form of digging.

The digging was hard work, and my shoulders are now aching, but I felt reinvigorated and much more prepared to tackle my afternoon workload. I think I was more productive too.

Whilst I'm predominantly working from home, I can try to do this a bit more. But I can't fit this into my life the way I was living before, along with so many other self-care necessities there just aren't enough hours in the day for.

I know that I can't go back to living that way, not if I want to stay well. So how do I fit in the stuff that's going to help me stay afloat? What do I stop doing?

Crikey that feels impossible to answer. I don't know how, but I need to rebalance my life whilst achieving all the same things! The project manager in me wants to make a plan with incremental improvements, whilst creative me wants to throw it all in the air and try something different. I expect the reality will fall somewhere between the two, once I'm well enough to try.

I feel like I'm holding my breath, waiting for a lifeline, but it's not coming. Every day teetering on the edge, not knowing if today's the day I'll fall over into that black hole.

Please send help.

H x

Day 15

I'm so tired! I feel so foggy-headed and lethargic that at any minute I could rest my head and sleep. It's hard feeling like this yet having to power through because there is work and home stuff. Plus I really should do some exercise because that's good for my mental health.

I feel like I could spend a week or two just sleeping. Even though the medication is helping me sleep it never feels like enough. Maybe I should just stay in bed, or at least rest for a while. That's what I'd do if I had the flu or something, so maybe it'd help my mind heal in the same way it helps my body heal.

It's been a beautiful day today – bright and sunny but cold. My favourite kind of winter day. I went for a walk with a friend and it was wonderful to connect. Walking makes talking so much easier for me and we covered everything from our mental health to *Women's Hour* and New Year fads.

I wish I could keep hold of the feeling I have when I'm with a close friend or family – carry it with me like a comforting scarf so that I always feel its warmth.

I'm so lucky to have such an amazing support network

who are always there for me. You understand that although I don't always feel well enough to come to stuff it's lovely to be invited and it's so hugely appreciated every time you reach out to me.

Please rest assured that I'm fighting my hardest to get well and not let you down. I'm still here and I will find my way back to you.

H x

Day 16

I got myself mentally prepared for my occupational health meeting at work today, only to have it moved to tomorrow at the last minute. I was so anxious about going into work for the meeting that I've been on an adrenaline come down and feel completely exhausted.

As a result, it's been difficult to concentrate on my work today but, as is often the case, out of my darkness rises something bright – I've finished a fundraising application for the charity I've set up, which I've been agonising over for ages.

A close friend pointed out to me that I always seem to create my most amazing achievements when I'm at my lowest. I've been reflecting on that and it really does seem to be the case. I wonder why? Maybe it's the desperation to find some light in all the darkness that opens up my mind to new possibilities.

Whatever the reason, I can keep a stash of these ideas to follow up on when I'm feeling better. I'm not sure when that will be.

I'm keeping everything crossed that I'll have some support and treatment options out of my occupational health meeting tomorrow. I also hope I'll hear from the Community Mental Health Team as they would have discussed my referral at their meeting today.

I'm desperate to have some help and a path to getting better. I've been feeling this way for so long now and I'm struggling to hang on and keep fighting the longer this takes. All I can do is take it a day at a time, even if I need to break each day down into manageable pieces... deep breaths, five more minutes...

H x

Day 17

I can barely function today. I am so utterly exhausted that I can't think straight, I can't even tell how I feel.

I should have gone to bed; my parents were here with us today, so I could have done. But I didn't. I'm really not sure why. I guess I'm not used to allowing myself to 'give in' and move away from the norm. Maybe I'm punishing myself for feeling this way. Whatever the reason, it's probably something I need to 'get over'. I'll add it to the list.

I had my occupational health meeting today at work. I feel like it's been an endless run of assessments whereby I'm required to sit in a bland hospital room and bare my soul for a complete stranger, begging for help, only to be referred on to someone else and for the cycle to continue.

What would be great is if there was one person I could build a relationship with and tell everything to so that they could identify the correct service for me and make all the introductions. There are so many standard questionnaires used for diagnosis and level of need that if we could create a process flow of services – something like 'if questionnaires indicate X then Y service is needed at level Z' then we could streamline the referral process and free up resources to actually help people.

I realise that any solution would need to be much more nuanced and refined but I honestly think it's possible. I'll add it to the 'to do' list for my charity The Mental Health Community (https://www.thementalhealthcommunity.co.uk).

Anyway, I need to find the energy to eat and then I can go to bed. Goodnight!

H x

Day 18

Another weekend begins. Two more days when I feel like a woefully inadequate wife and mother.

I managed to take the children to a birthday party today and it was so wonderful to see them running about, having fun with their friends. They had a brilliant time and I'm chuffed that I coped with taking them.

It was lovely to catch up with some friends at the party too. I know that I have isolated myself a bit because, frankly, I know I'm not much fun at the moment. I find it difficult to make conversation because my brain is foggy and slow, and I never know how to answer when people ask how I am. I am hugely lucky to have friends who accept me for who I am, even now, and will carry on including me regardless.

I'm so thankful for that.

I definitely needed some quiet time after the party and was able to shut myself away to do some crafting, which is great. I find it really mindful and it helps to clear my head of all the noise that's usually filling it.

I know that time spent this way needs to be part of my recovery and on into whatever new shape my life takes. But it's hard to take the time, it feels like I need to obtain permission; from myself, my husband, my children. I think I need to be stronger at taking this time that I so dearly need and protecting it. I'm not sure how to do that but I'll add it to the list of 'things that help' and hope to work with the Community Mental Health Team to turn that, plus therapy, into a treatment plan. I hope I get to see them soon.

H x

Day 19

I've actually managed some adulting today. I did the laundry and made a roast dinner. I know it's not much but it's more than I've managed in weeks.

It still feels unnatural to celebrate it, though. I mean, it really is no big deal for most people. It's just that at the moment this is a Herculean effort for me, which today I managed.

I've been thinking about how I can celebrate these wins

during my recovery but I'm struggling to come up with ideas. If you can think of anything, please get in touch via the contact information at the back of the book.

This all ties in with being able to give myself permission to do things to stay well and celebrating my successes. I'm speaking with a well-being coach at the moment. My goal is to achieve space and time in my life to focus on myself, be that self-care, time out or time to focus on a project I'm working on.

It's been really interesting to talk things through with an impartial listener. In just one session we identified a couple of tweaks to my weekly routine that would free up an hour to have for myself. I'm really looking forward to our next session.

I have in my mind that my treatment plan may follow a similar path; reviewing my life through the lens of my illness and using a variety of tools and techniques to treat, tweak and transform how I live so that I get well and stay well.

I'm not sure if the reality will match this idea, or even if I'll get seen by a professional at this rate. Fingers crossed that I hear from the Community Mental Health Team this week and can actually have some help!

H x

Day 20

Today has been a whirlwind of feeling overwhelmed, frustrated and frozen with fear.

Having said that, I have achieved quite a lot today: I

phoned around to see if I could hasten a response from the Community Mental Health Team, reviewed my occupational health report and asked for changes to be made so that it more accurately reflects our discussion and had a good solution-based therapy session. Oh, and I did a full day's work!

It's no wonder I'm exhausted when I'm trying to manage my anxiety to enable me to achieve all that, whilst trying to present as the confident, capable project manager that my employers know and expect.

I guess that's the problem in a nutshell; why on earth am I trying to continue as if nothing's wrong at work when the reality is that I feel like I'm having a complete breakdown?!

For me, it's partly because I take refuge in my work. I enjoy what I do and find having something to focus on – that I know I can do well – really helpful. It's also because I don't want to lose my job. I would really like my contract to be renewed in a couple of months and so I feel like I need to stay 'on it'.

The trick is going to be achieving the right balance of working, so I don't feel I'm letting people down, and rest/therapy/support so that I don't let myself down.

The problem I'm having is making sense of what that balance needs to be and having a plan to fit everything in. In part, that's because I've not seen the Community Mental Health Team yet and so don't know what they will recommend. But, also, in part because I'm struggling to think straight and trust my gut on what feels right.

I hope help comes soon.

H x

Day 21

At what point am I going to get help? I'm so bloody angry that I'm no closer to having any support than I was at the beginning.

Seriously, when you go to your GP and say, 'I'm having a breakdown, my symptoms are uncontrollable, and I've made a plan to end my life,' and more than four weeks and three assessments later I STILL HAVE NO TREATMENT PLAN!

FFS!

I know the NHS is stretched to breaking point and there's no money and no people to deliver services. I'm honestly not blaming anyone, but when you're desperate for help it's just so hard. I JUST NEED SOME HELP... PLEASE!

I am angry and vulnerable, desperate and desolate. Please, please I just need some help. Some sense that there is a way out of this, that there is light, hope for recovery. Without that there is no point, no reason to carry on fighting, no end to this nightmare.

I have nothing left to fight with.

H x

Day 22

I had a couple of meetings at work today, so went into the office for the first time since early December.

I'm not going to lie, it was really hard. I spent yesterday catastrophising about all the things that would happen when I went in and consequently had a disturbed night filled with anxious dreams.

This morning was so tough. I had to manage the anxiety and panic attacks enough to take the children to school then I had to try and regroup before heading in.

I think I spent most of the day shaking and trying to calm myself through distraction, breathing exercises and self-talk, all whilst trying to lead discussions and promote the work I'm doing.

I think I did okay. I mean, we had some productive work conversations and I made it through the day without having to leave or completely losing my shit, so I'm taking that as a win!

I'm totally exhausted now, though. I learnt today that about two hours is the maximum I can manage at the moment. After that it became significantly harder to stay focused and alert as the fatigue set in.

I'm glad I did it and I know that I need to try and aim for a little bit of time in the office each week so that it hopefully gets easier each time.

For now, I'm going to celebrate my win with some Netflix and chocolate followed by an early night.

H x

Day 23

I'm so exhausted. I don't mean tired, I mean full on, to the bone exhausted. I feel like I could sleep solidly for a week and still wake up tired.

I'm not really sure how to resolve this feeling because clearly what I'm doing isn't cutting it. But short of stopping work and, well, life, there's not much I can do. Just keep plodding on, I guess.

It's been hard to concentrate today. I think I overdid it in the office yesterday. Lesson learned – I'll try to do less next time and build up gradually.

I should probably go to bed at the same time as the kids, but that's the time I use to have tea and reset before it all starts again tomorrow.

Not that I have the energy to do anything in the evenings. I can barely hold a conversation, let alone contemplate going out or actually doing anything. It's pretty standard just to collapse on the sofa and stare at the television; I know it's not much but it's 'my' time. When I don't have to be anything for anyone else. It's time for me to reflect on the day, process everything and wind down ready for bed.

I'm trying to think about my energy and ability to do stuff in terms of Spoon Theory: every task requires a number of spoons, once used, spoons can only be replenished through rest. A person who runs out of spoons has no choice but to rest until their spoons are replenished. My resources are so low that I have very few spoons for each day and most of these are used up by just doing the basics (getting up and dressed, making and eating food, etc.).

I feel guilty that I don't get to see friends as much as I'd like, but I just don't have any spare spoons at the moment. They are all being spent on surviving.

Getting better will take even more spoons each day, so

I worry something else will have to give if I ever hear from the Community Mental Health Team, but that's a worry for another day.

H x

Day 24

I think the last few days have put me in a spoon deficit. I am really struggling just to get through each day. I'm relieved it's the weekend so I can hibernate a bit to try and recover.

I'm so tired of feeling like this. When I'm exhausted the intrusive thoughts[1] are harder to manage and the voice inside that's telling me there is another way – a permanent way – out of this is almost constant. I don't have enough energy to fight this.

The medication is helping me sleep better at night, yet I still feel utterly exhausted. How much more sleep do I need?!

It just all feels so frustrating and impossible right now. There's no sign of any support or treatment from the Community Mental Health Team yet, so it feels more and more that I need to plan and drive my recovery myself. I just don't have the headspace or energy to make a plan for that, let alone follow it through.

All I've got so far are some vague ideas: mineral and hormone level checks, eat better, exercise, sleep, therapy, more therapy, somehow balance my life better.

---

1   learn more about intrusive thoughts here: https://www.derbyshirehealthcareft.nhs.uk/perinatal/patients/worrying-intrusive-thoughts

So, in the interests of accountability, I'm going to make an appointment with my GP for the checks. Before that I will do a bit of reading to back up my request. The timings for this are a bit out of my control so my first action, which I'll do this weekend, is find a recipe and make some protein-packed granola bars. I can have these for breakfast or snacks to replace some of my mainly toast diet.

As I'm writing this, it feels overwhelming, but I know that to get better I need to take some action. Here goes…

H x

Day 25

I'm so angry all the time! I'm frustrated and snappy, I have virtually no patience and feel like there's an angry cloud filtering everything I say.

Even when I don't mean it to, things I say come out sounding angry. It means I'm not nice to be around, hell it's not even nice being in my head! I wish I knew how to make it stop.

There are so many 'side effects' of severe anxiety and depression: inability to focus, inability to make decisions, fatigue, intense anger, to name just a few. I'm trying to hide these because they are hard to explain, but it's impossible now. It's a vicious circle because I struggle to make a decision, or something I say comes out wrong and upsets someone, and then I get cross with myself for that and it all starts again.

I hate this.

All I can do is keep apologising and try to go easy on myself. It's hard to be compassionate to myself though, when I feel so far away from the person I've always been.

Maybe there will be a point at which I will feel like myself again. Right now, that doesn't feel possible. I know I need to take things one step at a time and that recovery is slow and not linear. It's just bloody frustrating that I can plan and accomplish most things I set my mind to, except my own recovery.

That's enough.

I can't be like this anymore. I'm sick of feeling hopeless and victimised by this illness, begging for support that's not coming.

I'm going to make a plan for my recovery.

H x

Chapter 3

A Smidge of Light

This part of the journey can feel tough – maybe you're out of the initial crisis and you've put some support in place to get you through the day-to-day... but you feel a million miles away from the person you recognise as yourself. It feels like you're walking a tightrope to try and keep the overwhelm in check, terrified of every sway and wobble on your journey. But look at how far you've already come. You're doing great, so just keep taking those tiny baby steps or stand still for a minute and breathe. This is the point in my journey where I got really angry. I felt let down by the lack of professional support and disappointed when whatever I'd researched was dismissed by the GP. I also felt thoroughly pissed off that I was feeling this way and my usual tactics of keeping my head down and ploughing through weren't working. This anger fuelled me to make some changes and actually take some leaps forward in getting to know myself and using that information to take control over my recovery.

Day 26

Everything is a little clearer today. I had a good rest and have had twenty-four hours where I've only had to think about myself. I knew the children were having a whale of a time with Nanny and Grandad, so there was no guilt either.

I've done a lot of reading: some research articles about the impact of vitamins, minerals and micro-nutrients in mental health and a great book about learning self-care.

Following my research, I've ordered a supplement to take and have set the intention to eat a little better than the mainly toast diet I'm currently on. As a first step, I've made some granola bars that are packed with good stuff like nuts, seeds and protein powder.

The reading I've done about self-care has made me see that I've been prioritising work over my recovery. It's what people have been telling me, but I didn't see it until today.

It's hard to shift that balance, as I don't want to call in sick, really. However, I am setting the intention that this week I will ensure there is time set aside each day for self-care. That might be rest, therapy or going for a walk; whatever I need.

First thing on my to do list when I log into work tomorrow is to book out that time and set a reasonable, prioritised work to do list, which will help me stay on track.

I know I'm likely to wobble and slip back into old habits but that's okay. I accept that it's part of the learning curve I'm on.

H x

Day 27

So today started well; I've got an appointment with the Community Mental Health Team next week and I've booked in hypnotherapy and some quieter well-being time into my calendar for the week.

But then I got sucked into work and, before I know it, the day is over and I am utterly exhausted. There's just so much to do and no one else to do it.

It'd be easy to sink into beating myself up over this but instead I'm going to make a concerted effort to focus on the positives: I have booked well-being time into my calendar, I have moved the project on a big leap today and I had an awesome bit of feedback! Someone I don't know very well said they always enjoy speaking to me because I make them feel inspired – what an awesome thing to hear!

In all seriousness, I know I need to try harder with focusing on my recovery every day and I will commit to doing that. There are still a good ten days until my Community Mental Health Team appointment, so I need to keep myself going and try to do a bit more research about various options and therapies so I can be prepared.

My allocated support worker will probably not expect to be presented with a project plan for my recovery but I have a feeling that's what she'll get! Ah well, if it helps me get the help I need, it'll be worth it.

I am definitely going to have a quieter day tomorrow, although I do have to go into the office, so I'll have to be disciplined about that.

Baby steps…
H x

Day 28

I feel like I'm full-on sprinting but never catching up to where I need to be. I know part of that is the job I do but I think it's also the amount of other stuff I'm trying to fit in.

Things at work are really busy. I'm supposed to be working reduced hours but can't even get everything done in my full hours! My 'to do' list is huge and there's real pressure for progress from the business that I'm struggling to juggle with the tasks and resources I have.

This is often how it goes with projects and usually I can ride it out and pull it all together. I'm worried I won't be able to this time and I'm struggling to accept that.

Just writing this down helps me to calm down and highlight my priorities. Hopefully I can feed that into my planning tomorrow.

I need to get better at saying no. Better at protecting time and headspace for myself. I need to find a way to reduce my mental load so that I can use that space for recovery. The trouble is, that needs me to be able to push back, say no, prioritise me and I'm just not good at that. I don't feel like I'm important enough to do that – I don't take priority over all the other stuff. I come last on the list.

Wow. If a friend said that to me, I'd be so quick to tell her that she DOES come first! How can she do all the other things that 'life' needs without looking after herself?

That she IS important. So why can't I do that for myself?!

Because this is what I've always done.

I'm an 'obliger'; I make things happen and I support others to achieve what they need to. I have unrealistically high expectations of myself and live in fear of letting people down.

I need to redress the balance. But how?

H x

Day 29

What a day! I am full of cold and have had a full day of meetings, so I'm exhausted but actually feeling okay.

I had a really good therapy session today and we hit on what I feel is a fundamental belief. It's something that I can trace a lot of my anxious thoughts back to, it drives a lot of my unhealthy, unhelpful behaviours and, if you unpick all the things I feel about myself, it all boils down to this.

I am not enough.

I am not enough.

It's really stark written down. It's hard for me to even say those words out loud but bloody hell I feel them at the very centre of my being.

I have no idea when this started, or what started it. But in recovery terms it's huge that I now recognise this. It's something to unpick further, to gently coax out into the light so that I can study it and start to nudge it into a healthier sense of being.

I know that I can provide evidence of my worth,

examples of times I have been enough. But I also know that's not enough to change this. Things will only get better, properly better (not sticking plaster better) once my belief changes. When I truly feel that I am enough. Enough for me, for my family, enough to take up space in the world.

There's a long way to go.

H x

Day 30

I can't believe it's day thirty. I've been so focused and living such a small life that so much time has gone without me really noticing.

I feel like I've retreated into my head a bit, not really engaging with the outside world and minimising social interactions. I think that's partly self-preservation – trying to conserve the limited energy I have – and partly because I'm ashamed. I don't want my friends and family to turn away from me, or be disappointed or upset by the reality of my illness and lack of progress towards recovery.

In reality, I know that my friends and family love me and wouldn't dream of turning away, but I can't stop that fear.

How do we get to a point where there is no shame? Where you can talk about mental illness as easily as a broken bone or the flu? I honestly don't know. I'm challenging myself to talk openly about how I feel and what's happening, and no one is responding with anything but support.

It's like the shame is already ingrained within me. I'm not sure how to change that, except by continually challenging myself to have the tough conversations.

I'm reassured to learn that mental health is being talked about at school and the children are learning how to keep mentally well. I am supporting this at home by openly telling the children that my mental health isn't good at the moment and that I'm getting help to get well.

I hope that's enough to prevent the shame growing inside them.

H x

REGROUP

Regrouping is all about reconnecting with yourself and your dreams. Not so you can sit and wallow in how unachievable it all feels, but so that you can open yourself up again to the possibility of living a different way, to remind yourself of your potential and reconnect with love.

When we're experiencing dark times, we are overrun with fear. Every thought, situation and perception we have is guided by that fear. Our natural reaction is to run from that fear. To avoid situations and people that make the fear worse. We want to hide away, minimise our pain until it goes away.

Whilst it's totally okay to do this for a while, it won't solve anything in the long term.

Hiding away won't address the fear or kick it back into touch. Just like the school or workplace bully, we have to stand up to our fear. We need to confront it, let it into our hearts so that we can win it over, turn it into love. This isn't easy to do, particularly if you don't yet understand what your trigger is. Once you have that statement of fear that drives all your experiences and behaviours you can start to move forward.

Tools that helped me to identify my fear statement are: CBT (Cognitive Behavioural Therapy), *The Universe Has your Back*, talking it through. Your fear statement can be found in the words of your inner critic.

Mine is: I am not enough.

Once you have this key piece of information, you can start to work through it. Every time you feel unable to leave the house, or you've lost your temper over an innocuous comment from a loved one, you can take a minute, breathe through the fear and understand that your reactions are being driven by that.

The more you do this, the more you call out your fear and identify your usual responses, you start to build a new way forward. You can start to shift away from internalising the blame and fear, understanding that it's not who you are. Your fear is just that – an emotion that's somehow taken root and is feeding itself from your response to it.

It's hard and uncomfortable, but once you

start calling it out and modifying your reactions, it becomes easier, until it's a new habit and you don't need to think about it so much. Remember: you are not your fear. Take baby steps and, slowly but surely, you'll start to change your fear into love.

Each time you notice that you're reacting from a place of fear, ask yourself what a reaction from a place of love would be. What would you tell a friend facing this situation to do? Would you tell them to run away, scream or shout? Or would you support and encourage them to go gently, be compassionate and have love for themselves?

When you're looking for tools to help you regroup, focus on connecting with your heart and what makes it sing. It can be anything that gives you hope, inspires you to cling on to life and helps you see that you are not alone.

For me, regrouping means looking outwards for inspiration: TED talks, online articles, books, podcasts, social media groups. I learn from other people's stories, how they are working to better shape themselves and the world they live in.

I take in the positivity of what others share, feel outraged by the prejudice they experience or awed by the action they are taking. I use these feelings to reconnect with my true self, the person I want to be, the person I know I am underneath the fear.

"When you recover or discover something that

nourishes your soul and brings joy, care enough about yourself to make room for it in your life."

Jean Shinoda Bolen

What are your regroup activities? (Find the worksheet at the website: https://www.themental healthcommunity.co.uk/tools)

Day 31

Parenting is hard. Even when I'm well, the constant need for attention, bickering and whinging can test my patience. But, right now, I'm finding it almost impossible.

It's like I don't have the headspace to process everything they need from me and present the 'happy mum' face they expect. I'm not sure how to get more headspace, though, given that the majority of it is used up trying to calm my anxiety or answer the negative self-talk.

I guess it'll come as I get better. Not sure when that might be at this point. Recovery feels like an almost intangible cloud hovering just out of reach.

I feel like I'm drowning under the weight of all this. It's been going on so long I feel the pressure to 'get better' and be back to my usual self is growing. But this time I can't save myself; I need several life rings and a boat to shore.

Until then I'm treading water like mad, trying desperately not to go under. I'm hanging on to people around me to keep myself afloat and I'm scared to let go.

H x

Day 32

I've been snappy and horrible today. I know I'm doing it, but I just can't stop, which is making me cross with myself and probably perpetuating that behaviour.

I took myself into town this afternoon to try and clear my head. I find walking in the fresh air really restorative and it helps me to order my thoughts. Plus, the distraction of a bit of window shopping helps prevent me getting stuck in an angry loop.

I feel frustrated at not having a treatment plan yet, at not being in regular therapy to help address the issues. But I also feel frustrated because I should be doing more to help myself – I just don't have the headspace.

It was only after I talked it through with a friend that I realised it: that's the whole point! If I wasn't so unwell, I'd be doing all those things, but I am ill, so it's not as easy as that. I need to accept that and give myself a break. I think because I'm really good at faking being well for short periods of time, I am expecting more of myself.

This has to stop.

I even heard myself say, 'I'm supposed to be working reduced hours, but I don't have the time.' How ridiculous is that?! No one is going to die if it takes a bit longer to get my work done. But if I keep pushing and resisting taking the time I need to get better, there is the distinct possibility that I might.

Time to change that.

H x

Day 33

It's the end of another weird, slightly strained weekend. The children know that I'm not right and to be honest I think we're all a bit fed up with it.

I feel so guilty for the impact this is having on my family, but I also feel angry, frustrated, exhausted, isolated and very alone. It's almost like I'm trapped in a box – I can see everything that's going on and people can see me, but we can't quite reach each other to interact.

I know that I need to find the fire inside me again. The fire that means I stand up for myself and what I believe in and watch out if you get in my way! I know the fire is still there, it's just smouldering at the moment as it fuels my survival. That I've made it this far is a testament to the strength of it.

Today I'm going to fuel that fire a bit more. I'm going to stand up for myself because even though, right now, I don't believe I deserve it, my family needs me to. I can't make huge changes or big decisions at the moment, but I can take teeny, tiny micro steps in the right direction.

The first step for me is to say no. No to putting work before my mental health. No to cramming in another meeting or task because it's good for the project. No.

I have a course all day tomorrow and then presentations for the next two days. It's going to be tough going so I am blocking out recovery time this week. Every day, at least an hour of mental health time to help me get through the week. That time, coupled with a 'to do' list to delegate, are my first micro steps to getting back to me.

H x

Chapter 4

Recovery Isn't Linear

It's important to recognise that recovery isn't going to be a straight line from feeling bad to feeling better. This can feel like the end of the world (it did for me as you'll see in this chapter), so it's vital to reach out, increase your support and self-care and dial back on any pressure you're putting on yourself. During these days I lost hope, felt let down and almost back where I started. Until I realised that this is what happens with any major change.

Think about it; when your work tries to bring in a new computer system for everyone to use it's not all sunshine and rainbows. Some people's first reaction is usually something along the lines of: "We don't need that, what we've been using is fine!" Then as the system rolls out, everyone starts training and having to use it and they become frustrated at having to "waste time learning something new". That frustration can turn into disruption – angry meetings with bosses telling them how rubbish the new system is. But as more people start to use the new system, the word gets out that "it's not too bad once you get the hang of it" and gradually those naysayers start giving it a go and realising it's actually okay. Before you know it, the system is fully embedded (until you need to replace it in a few years' time, and everyone has to go through the cycle again!).

Understanding the stages you're likely to go through and accepting that there are going to be setbacks along the way can help you stay on track. Build up a toolkit to get you through those trickier times, that by acknowledging the wave and doing what you can to help it wash over you, you can survive it.

Day 34

Awful night's sleep last night, full of anxious dreams ahead of a busy work week – full day course followed by two days of presentations.

So not a great start to the day and I had to use most of my spoons just to get to the course for a 9am start.

Mornings are definitely the hardest part of the day for me. It's almost like I need to spend the first few hours distracting myself until I've proved that whatever catastrophe I was predicting isn't going to happen.

But I did it! I made it to the course, held it together all day and even managed to participate in some of the discussions. The negative self-talk was high throughout and I found myself constantly questioning what right I had to be there and what value I could add.

But I did it! That is a huge achievement for me, and I'm trying to recognise and celebrate that.

I'm still committed to carving out recovery time for myself and protecting that time. I'm lucky enough to have a supportive manager and so I discussed this with him today.

He's completely on board and will help me to identify the additional resources needed to make this happen. I just need to not let the negative self-talk take over and push me back into bad habits.

I have a rare moment of peace at home alone, so I am going to make a cuppa and read my book. I am definitely not going to do any of the jobs that need doing. They can wait!

H x

Day 35

I'm really feeling the effects of two work days where I've had to be 'on it'. I am utterly exhausted, I feel shaky, tense, emotional and I am really having to do battle with the intrusive thoughts.

I just feel like such a failure. I'm not able to do things that I've always done, none of my coping mechanisms work and I feel like I'm just letting people down all the time.

I'm having such a hard time being strong with work. I know I should be working reduced hours but it's really hard to have that conversation with everyone who needs to know. I feel like I may as well put up a huge sign apologising for my failure.

When is this going to feel better?

H x

Day 36

Boundaries, boundaries, boundaries.

Boundaries are such tricky things. When they are wonky it can have an impact on all areas of our lives. I'm really struggling to set clear boundaries and enforce them.

This probably stems from my 'I'm not enough' core driver because I'm always striving to be more so that I don't let people down. It doesn't help that I'm an obliger[2] by personality type, which means I struggle to be accountable to myself for what's important to me.

I had plans to speak with my manager today about working reduced hours, as recommended by occupational health. But when I got to the meeting, we started talking about work stuff and then I felt too awkward to bring it up.

I just don't feel strong enough to assert my boundaries right now. The trouble is, no one can do that for me.

How do I do this?

I just need to do it. There are so many negative consequences if I don't do it. I need to stop putting on the 'I'm fine' mask and ask for what I need.

Bloody hell, this would be so much easier if I had some professional support, a treatment plan, anything.

I can't help but dread my appointment with the Community Mental Health Team. I've been waiting so long for help and I fear there will be a longer wait after the appointment before I actually get access to any.

Deep breaths, I can't lose hope now. Just hang on for

---

2   See Gretchen Rubin's 4 personality types https://quiz. gretchenrubin.com/four-tendencies-quiz/

one more day (and then one day after that, one day after that and onwards) until I don't feel like this anymore.

H x

Day 37

I've really struggled today; this week has exhausted me. But as I close my laptop for the weekend, I feel a little bit proud of myself. I've put a plan in place to cover the work of the project and sent it to my boss outlining my plan for working reduced hours.

I've found this such a difficult conversation to have face to face, so I have written it in an email and will follow up with a discussion next week. I'm so glad it's done. I know I need to put it into practice and work on my boundaries, but this feels like a good step.

I'm pleased I feel positive and I'm hoping that feeling stays with me through tomorrow and my Community Mental Health Team appointment. I know I'm going to need every ounce of strength I have to get through the meeting for the help I need.

I'm dreading the appointment. I have all kinds of scenarios running through my head with accompanying intrusive thoughts and, of course, all the fun of severe anxiety.

I'm scared because I've felt so raw, so vulnerable for so long now that I'm able to mask it more and more. The trouble with that is the more I mask, the harder it is to drop the mask for fear of the reality beneath.

It's the feeling that if I start to open up and let the darkness out it'll consume everything, and I'll never find my way out of it.

I guess that's what therapy is for.

H x

Day 38

I feel numb; I've retreated inside my head because the fire in me has gone out and I've lost hope.

My support worker was lovely but because I don't meet the criteria for top level care (because I have a family to support me) we will have to muddle along completing CBT (cognitive behavioural therapy) worksheets that she's printed from the internet.

I'm sure when/if I make it out of this hole, I'll see the value in this. But, right now, it feels like someone has cut the last thread that was holding me onto this world.

I'm sure there's anger in there somewhere, buried under the foggy darkness. Anger that because I use work as a distraction and am lucky enough to have a supportive family that I don't qualify for more help. None of that support stops the thoughts or the need to end this hell.

By not qualifying for more help, I'm just a bigger burden on my family.

One they don't need.

H x

Day 39

I didn't sleep well last night. I really struggled with intrusive thoughts as I tried to make sense of my feelings after the appointment yesterday.

It's fair to say I feel disappointed, vulnerable and alone. I feel the full weight of my recovery sits with me at a time when I don't have the strength to handle it.

But as I was awake in the small hours fighting the urge to sneak out and lose myself on the moors until the cold did its work, I decided to weigh up the pros and cons.

That's right: I made a list of pros and cons to ending my life. I realise how bonkers this is. But whilst it was difficult to think straight and discern between what's true and what are intrusive thoughts, I came to a decision.

I don't want to die.

Ending my life feels like the only way of achieving peace and being free of this darkness. But I owe it to myself and my family to give recovery another shot.

I've spent the day thinking about the steps I can take towards recovery and my husband has been researching therapy options.

This evening we're going to make a plan to ease the stresses at home and for therapy and life changes that will help me get back to myself again.

It's going to be challenging and we've less support from the Community Mental Health Team than we'd hoped, but this is what we've got, so we need to make it work.

Wish me luck!

H x

I feel it's important to pop a reminder here... if you feel affected or triggered by anything you are reading then please reach out and talk to someone. At the back of this book is a list of organisations who may be able to help.

Day 40

Another unsettled night, full of anxious dreams and intrusive thoughts, so I'm tired today but resolute.

Making a recovery plan is a daunting task. I'm taking it a step at a time, so it hopefully won't overload me. I've also asked for help; help with ideas for things to aid my recovery and for help to actually deliver those things.

My first steps were emailing work to confirm my plan for working reduced hours and asking my husband to take responsibility for the food shopping.

I've asked my yogi friend to help me find my mantra and recommend some good restorative yoga flows for me to try.

I've also looked up some new podcasts to listen to – podcasts about mental health, about accepting yourself as you are and one about starting my own happiness project, which I guess is what I'm doing really!

It's a good start and I'm really lucky to have a great support network to help me. I just need to try and accept that this is who I am, that there will be times that I struggle. But hopefully in doing this I will build a toolkit to help me through those times and shape my life to minimise them.

I also need to accept that struggling isn't failing. That I can build a life and be happy, even with this illness.

There's a long way to go.

H x

Day 41

Ugh. I am really not feeling it today. I'm tired – it appears whatever effect the medication was having on my sleep is now diminishing, so I'm having disturbed nights again.

I'm also struggling with the weight of work for my recovery. It feels like there's so much to do and I don't have the right help. Maybe that'll change when I actually start my appointments with the support worker, but to be honest I don't have a lot of hope.

I feel like I want to get in bed and just never leave it. I keep reminding myself to take it one step at a time and that they can be baby steps when I need them to be. The trouble is, I just want to be better. I'm really frustrated that I'm still feeling like this.

I know I have improved – I'm eating regularly (albeit a limited menu), I'm leaving the house a bit and I'm not randomly crying all the time. But the thoughts haven't changed; I'm still struggling to deal with them and don't yet understand how to.

This feels like a lot of responsibility to carry for someone who barely feels capable of getting out of bed. I really wish there was a bit more support from the professionals. From someone who knows the illness and the different variations of what recovery looks like. I don't think that's too much to ask.

Well clearly it is because that doesn't appear to be what I've got.

Oh balls.

H x

Day 42

I woke up in a really awful mood this morning. I felt really angry and was really struggling to manage the intrusive thoughts, which meant I had no headspace to deal with any real-world stuff.

Of course, then the guilt sets in and it's a vicious circle from then on. Luckily, a friend came over and we went for a walk. Well, more of a stomp through the countryside. It was drizzly and muddy but the combination of fresh air, walking and a good friend to talk to did wonders for my mood.

I feel like this should be part of my recovery and long-term plan to stay well because it really does make a huge difference. I realise it's not something I could fit in every day, but I think I could manage it weekly.

Now I just need to find something to help me deal with the intrusive thoughts. Hopefully the work I'm going to do with the support worker will help with that. I've had a look at the first CBT workbook she printed off for me and it talks about the cycle of thoughts, feelings and behaviours.

I've got some homework to do before my appointment on Monday, but I need to pick my timings carefully as looking at the intrusive thoughts and my behaviour pattern closely has a tendency to make things worse for a bit before I see any improvement. I remember this from the CBT I had to address my post-natal depression.

I have workshops to run for the next two days, so I'll look at it all after that. Need to keep my game face on for work!

H x

Day 43

I was in the office today running a workshop. It went well and we had some really positive engagement, but I can still tell that I'm off my game. Things don't flow as they usually would and I'm having to work harder to get the usual results from myself.

Consequently, after four hours, I was totally exhausted and needed to come home to rest. As I've been reflecting on my performance, all the niggles are surfacing. They're probably not anything that others would notice but now they're in my head I can't stop thinking about them.

I should be able to handle this better.

I'm really frustrated with myself. I just need to get out of my own way – I'm the one not working reduced hours, I'm the one struggling to implement my self-care activities. No one is stopping me, so why can't I do it?

How the hell am I supposed to learn to accept that this

is always going to be part of my life? I don't want to live with this. I WANT IT TO GO AWAY.

H x

CHANGE CURVE

In my professional life I have done a lot of work with the Kubler-Ross change curve from an organisational perspective. I find it incredibly useful to reference this both for myself and for those affected by any change I am delivering and I use it to inform my approach and communication style. The change curve shows the six stages that we use to process change. It's not a step-by-step process, but can be really helpful in understanding what you need in order to move forward. The starting point is Denial: where we're looking for evidence that the change isn't the right thing to do. Here we need to seek more information about the change. This is followed by Frustration: where we are starting to accept that things are changing, but we're really not happy about it. This can then lead to Depression and for both of these stages the most helpful approach is to find support. As we start to accept the change we move to Experiment and need time to explore and test the change. Once we've tested the waters we make a Decision: we learn how to work with the change and start feeling positive. The final stage is Integration: where the change becomes the 'new normal' and it's time to celebrate!

You can find more on the change curve here: https://www.ekrfoundation.org/5-stages-of-grief/change-curve/

It was only when I started noticing how frustrated I was with myself and the situatuion I was in that I realised the change curve could apply here too. I found that referencing the change curve and identifying where I currently was on it really helped give me clarity and peace. For example, if I'm in the frustrated phase, I know that it'll help me if I rest and then talk to people about how I'm feeling and what is frustrating me. I can remind myself to just be supportive and listen to what my body and mind are trying to say, so that I can best work out how to move forward.

Have a think about the change curve, where do you think you currently are? How can you change your internal dialogue to better support your movement through the curve?

Chapter 5

Slow Progress

In this chapter I'm starting to make some real progress, which was hard to see at the time, but as I look back over these journal entries there's a definite shift. I know more about myself and what works for me, I'm clearer about taking the time and activities that help me recover from a tough day and I'm feeling able to do more. I found it hard not to overdo it on 'good' days, trying to make up for lost time or just making the most of feeling lighter. It's critical to take things steady and make time to rest. Celebrate the lighter days and carry them close to help you through the darker ones. Remember that lasting change takes time – there is no quick fix, so stick with it and make sure you take time to reflect on just how far you've come, warrior.

Day 44

I'm glad this working week is over. It's been busy and I've felt enormous guilt for taking even tiny snippets of time to recover. But the key thing is I have taken the time. It's only about an hour a day, which is less than occupational health recommended, but it's a good start.

I definitely need to do some work on boundaries, I'll raise this with my therapist tomorrow. I have three more sessions with her before I'm left with just the support worker and I want to make the most of them.

I'm starting my CBT homework tonight, ready for my support worker appointment on Monday. I really hope it goes better than I am expecting! Right now, I still feel frustrated and let down by the service and that's not the best way to build trust with a therapist. I'm going to need to get my thoughts in order before the appointment.

We've got a busy weekend with a couple of kids' birthday parties. It'll be lovely for the children as they really enjoy parties and a chance to play with their friends. I am going to be strong about taking time out for myself to rest and recover afterwards, though, as I find parties exhausting.

I feel so antisocial at the moment, but I am really struggling to socialise. It's hard to put on a happy face but equally I don't want to bring everyone else down!

I have to keep reminding myself that it's time for baby steps, not big leaps. And then I have to remind myself to be kind, not cross and frustrated with myself, for only managing baby steps (and sometimes not even managing that!).

This is hard!

H x

Day 45

I'm feeling really vulnerable right now. I've been to a therapy session this morning where we talked about boundaries. We talked about my inability to say no to people, be that work, home, the kids, anything. This wonky boundary means I stretch myself too thin and that's when unhelpful behaviours kick in.

The other area where my boundaries are really out of whack is with myself. This manifests in a lot of negative self-talk and avoidance behaviour. It's why I can turn exciting things like trips out, seeing friends and holidays into things that I fear rather than the highlights they really are.

This boundary is something I've built up to 'protect' myself from the intrusive thoughts and anxiety. I recognise that it's misguided and that this really isn't protecting me, it's preventing me getting well and moving forward.

The biggest issue with breaking down this boundary is that I just don't want to. I feel vulnerable and unsafe, so the thought of taking down my protection is terrifying. I can't possibly open myself up to things I've spent years avoiding or limiting at a time when my reserves of strength are so low.

It's really frightening to think about opening myself up to even more vulnerability, but I know the rewards are potentially huge. I can't even imagine what it would be like to look forward to something. To be actually excited and focused on the good rather than being filled with dread and forcing myself to do it anyway.

I can't imagine it, but it sounds wonderful.
I want that.
H x

Day 46

I've been busy creating this afternoon. I took the children to a birthday party this morning, so earned myself some me-time!

I love tinkering with my collection of beads, buttons and other pretty things. It's great when inspiration hits and I can see a clear vision of something to create. I find the actual making really mindful and for a while my thoughts are calm and focused.

Until I'm finished.

I stare at the finished product and instead of joy and pride in what I've created, disappointment sets in. The ugly voice in my head starts listing flaws and comparing it to products seen elsewhere, highlighting how my creation falls short.

I can't make the voice stop. Eventually I give in and shove whatever I've made into a cupboard, never to see the light of day again.

Honestly, it's ridiculous! I love creating things, yet I inevitably end up miserable. I know this ugly voice in my head is mine, but I can't make it stop. It's something I'm plagued by in all areas of my life and can't just 'shake off'.

I wish there was an off switch!

Hopefully the work I'll be doing in therapy to straighten

up my boundaries and reset the unhealthy thoughts will help with this. Maybe it'll eventually quieten that ugly voice for good.

It'd be nice to feel proud of myself and my work. Even just once.

H x

Day 47

It's been a double kids' party weekend. I love that the children have such a fab time, but I wish I didn't find parties so difficult, especially at the moment.

I really feel the pressure to talk and build relationships with the parents. I mean, our children will go up through the school with these kids, so there are many more parties and play dates to come.

I didn't succeed at that today. But I'm determined not to spend the evening berating myself for it.

I spent a lovely evening yesterday with my fabulous yogi friend. We talked through some mantras and affirmations and how I can use them. We also worked through some restorative yoga poses that I can start to use.

I left her house feeling very peaceful and with hope that I can implement these tools to help my recovery. It's a great feeling, especially knowing that this is an area I can grow and adapt to suit each stage of my recovery.

I used my mantra for today to stay calm during the party and I'm looking forward to choosing one to suit my day tomorrow. It's nice to have something positive to focus my thoughts on when intrusive thoughts or images creep in.

I know it's going to take a lot of practice to train my mind to use these tools automatically, but I've taken the first step today.

H x

Day 48

I've had a really mixed day today. I'm exhausted after a terrible night's sleep and busy day of meetings, but I feel positive following my first actual session with the support worker.

We had a good chat about how things are at the moment and delved more into the intrusive thoughts. After our session last week, she'd found some additional resources and potential new avenues for us to follow, so I'm hopeful of actually getting somewhere.

For today we looked at some CBT worksheets and how I can use them to capture some of the intrusive thoughts. It'll be interesting to review it with her next week, but I'm scared about actually writing them down. I think it'll be hard to focus on them so closely and I worry that it'll make my coping rituals and anxiety worse for a while. I know that I need to do it regardless, otherwise I won't get better.

We also talked about testing out some of the intrusive thoughts to try and reinforce that the thoughts don't have power. This feels really daunting and something we'll definitely take slowly. I need to feel stronger before I can tackle this but it's good to know what's coming!

I've got a huge day at work tomorrow so I'm just preparing my affirmation for the day. I hope that this helps bring me positivity, focus and strength for the day.

For now, I'm going to try to have a restorative evening and fingers crossed for a decent sleep!

H x

Day 49

What a day! I ran an all-day workshop for my project board to bring them up to speed with what the project has been doing and prompt some decision making. It felt like an all-day sales pitch; I was pitching both the project and me.

I've been dreading this for a while and knew I'd be almost uncontrollably anxious. Last night I prepared my affirmation for the day: I am ready to go big, rise up and step into my power. I wrote it in my phone calendar for the day and set alerts for every hour. I also set it to pop up as my alarm went off this morning, so it'd be the first thing I looked at.

I took a few minutes first thing to sit in a restorative yoga pose whilst connecting with my breath and running my affirmation through my head.

I honestly feel this has really helped me today. I've been able to run the day and stay focused because every time an intrusive thought or anxiety has popped up I've brought my focus back to my breathing and affirmation. This has enabled me to move past the intrusive thoughts and continue my pitch.

I'm still using the practice now to fight the negative thoughts and overly critical self-review of my performance today that inevitably creeps in when I'm done.

For me, it doesn't work to 'accept the thought and move past it' or try to fight the thoughts with logic. But today this affirmation practice has really helped and I'm looking forward to choosing my affirmation for tomorrow, although I think it'll be something restorative given that I'll still be utterly exhausted!

H x

Day 50

Today has been a bit of a write-off. I'm so exhausted from yesterday that my brain is a total fog, and my body is aching all over.

I've really struggled to do any self-care activities or my therapy homework. I've certainly not been as productive at work as I'd have liked to be.

I realise that it's days like this that self-care should take priority but I'm at a loss as to how to make that happen. I'm just too exhausted to focus on my affirmation or go for a walk.

I feel like I should be doing more to help myself on days like this, but I just can't at the moment. I'm clearly doing something wrong or missing some key piece that unlocks that ability.

I feel like a failure today.

Fingers crossed that tomorrow is better.

H x

Day 51

I've been crying for most of the day. It's still the exhaustion from earlier in the week; I definitely put myself in severe spoon deficit and haven't given myself enough recovery time.

I spent the morning feeling useless and cross with myself for not being able to do anything helpful. I honestly just wanted to go back to bed. But I pulled on my superhero pants and headed out of the door to my therapy session.

It was a really tough session. I cried a lot, but we worked through some good stuff. I now understand a bit better how I self-sabotage, particularly around self-care and my recovery.

I understand that I do truly know who I am and what I need but that I don't value myself enough to follow it up. I just keep pushing and pushing myself to do more, try harder, be better because I don't feel enough.

We talked about how I could start to take baby steps towards allowing myself to do what I need and valuing the voice inside that's trying to help me.

It starts tonight, with me caring enough about myself to spend the evening doing something I enjoy instead of slumping in front of rubbish TV.

I know that 'no plan survives contact with the enemy', so it remains to be seen if I can manage not to self-sabotage. I know this is key to my recovery, so I really want to try and crack it.

H x

Day 52

It's amazing the difference a good block of sleep and a sunny day make. I woke up feeling replenished and seeing the glorious weather just perked me up enough to get me outside.

Once outside it was easy to find things to do to make the most of the sun. I even ate my lunch outside! The sun just helps me feel hopeful, I don't understand why, but I love the feeling.

The result is that I've had a pretty positive day. I've been kinder to myself, been able to play a bit with the children and have struggled less with the intrusive thoughts.

I just want to hold on to this feeling and carry it into tomorrow. I can't control the weather (that would be a great superpower!) but I can make sure I go to bed early and set myself up for good sleep.

I think I'll prep my affirmation for tomorrow and have a think about something I can do to be kind to myself. Recovery is a long, slow process and 'you can't boil the ocean' as they say. So, I just need to be kind to myself and celebrate all the little wins along the way.

I'm definitely celebrating today.

H x

Day 53

I've spent a lot of time reflecting today. I'm trying to understand what the blocker to changing my mindset is.

It's been a difficult day of delving deep and confronting things that I've worked hard to bury.

My workbook today has given me a new perspective to learn, looking at everything from a place of love. I'm projecting a lot of fear, anger and stress because I perceive everything as a challenge or threat, even when that's not how it was intended.

I do feel more serene now. I understand that my mindset and approach have been forged by fear and that I need to re-learn everything from a place of love.

I know that sounds 'hippy' and 'fluffy' but actually the approach really resonates with me, so I am embracing it fully. There are many more chapters in the book I'm reading for me to work through and I'm looking forward to seeing what else I learn.

It's a lot of work to change the habits of a lifetime but I know that I am ready to do that now. I am committed to changing how I view myself and the world around me and intend to enjoy the practice as much as I can.

H x

Day 54

I find it hard to talk about what I'm doing in therapy because it all feels raw and I feel vulnerable. I also worry that people will smirk at it as being 'fluffy nonsense', which will lead to me getting defensive and snappy.

I am going through a process of understanding and facing my fears. These fears have been driving me for years and it's difficult to face up to them, but I need to do that in order to change them.

My biggest fear is that I'm not enough: not enough as a wife/mother/friend/person. Not kind/funny/smart/successful/attractive enough… I could go on, but you get the picture.

Facing up to that is hard. Even though I've known what the fear is, I've never truly faced up to it and felt the weight of it in order to properly move past it.

I am starting to understand how my actions and behaviours are guided by fear and I need to change that. I need to learn how to face my fear and change my perception to one of love.

I need to learn to have love and compassion for myself instead of anger and hatred. I need to face every situation and recognise my fear, own the feelings and then guide my perception to one of love.

It's early in my journey and I'm overwhelmed by the feelings, but I'm working through them. I'm working to alter my perception, reassure myself that I am enough. That events/words/actions are not evidence of my failings, they are just triggers for my fear, which I can face with love.

H x

Day 55

I'm really feeling angry with the health service today! I've been left to cope with this by myself for the most part and as such I've done a lot of research about therapies, support and elements that have an impact on mental health. I went to my doctor today to check in and to ask for additional support, as what I've got isn't enough. The answer: No.

What upsets and angers me the most is that there was no reason offered. My ideas (backed up by evidence) were dismissed out of hand. The only additional support I was offered was to increase the dose of the medication I'm taking.

Seriously, I don't want to take so much medication that I'm numb to everything. It must cost the NHS more to throw pills at me than it would for a course of therapy. Surely it would be more cost effective to offer therapy and support as a means of sustainable recovery than to medicate me for the rest of my life?!

Anyway, enough ranting. I need to remember the work I'm doing and try to perceive this with love rather than the fear that I've got minimal support and will always feel like this.

I recognise that my anger is an expression of fear and in guiding myself towards a perception of love I could see this as a way to recognise my strength and capability to be enough for myself.

I've made it this far and I can see small improvements from the work I'm doing. Maybe I can be enough.

Crikey, it's uncomfortable to sit with these feelings, to accept them and guide my perception more positively, but it really does help clear my mind.

Hopefully it'll get easier with practice.

H x

Day 56

I woke up feeling clearer today. I celebrate days like this where my brain is working and I am able to focus on things.

I've processed my feelings from yesterday and I'm focused on my recovery again. It sounds a bit unlikely, but affirmations are really helping me. It's helpful to have something positive to focus on for each day and I'm building up a memory bank of them to use when intrusive thoughts or anxiety hit.

I had a panic attack this evening and used my affirmation to help me meditate and process the anxiety and symptoms. I'm still learning and there's a long way to go before I get the hang of this. But I recognise that it's helpful and I'm doing the practice.

My yogi friend is coming over this evening and we're going to work out a restorative yoga sequence that I can practice. I find yoga really mindful so I'm looking forward to our practice tonight and building it in to my recovery routine.

I'm so relieved to have found some tools that help now and with practice will help me sustain recovery enough to tackle some of the bigger stuff.

Fingers crossed some of this positivity rubs off on my therapy provision!

H x

Day 57

Anxiety hangovers are real.

I was literally shaking with anxiety this morning ahead of running a big workshop, this is pretty standard for me and, whilst I'm not sure I'll ever feel blasé about it, it's not usually this bad.

However, my anxiety is dominating at the moment, so naturally it affects this too. But no matter how often this happens, I'm always surprised by the anxiety hangover.

It's like I just hit a wall: my brain freezes, my body starts to hurt everywhere and I can barely keep my eyes open.

I understand the mechanics of it – the high stress, high anxiety wears off and I need to recover. This is why I still can't do a full day in the office without taking a day to get over it.

I'd like to work out a little routine for days like this so I can make sure I look after myself a bit better. It's always too hard to cook a proper dinner or do anything active, so I usually end up eating rubbish and slumped on the sofa, which probably isn't great for my recovery.

I'm going to try a long hot shower followed by some restorative yoga poses – nothing active, just calming. After that I might be able to face making proper food. But, if not, then that's okay for now. Baby steps.

Thank goodness for a quiet day tomorrow.

H x

Day 58

I'm really pleased that my recovery plan yesterday helped me to wake up feeling okay today. It's been a sunny day too, which always makes me feel better.

I managed to take the children to the park this afternoon and we had a great time running around and playing. I feel really pleased that I've managed to have some fun with them.

I had the penultimate session with my solution-based therapist today too. It's hard because I feel like there's so much work we need to do, but I've used up all the sessions allocated by work, plus a few extra they were able to give.

I'm really lucky that I've been able to access this through work. It's really helped me make progress, which I wouldn't otherwise have done given that my sessions with the support worker are only just starting.

I worry that without the solution-based therapy my recovery will stall, but I guess I'm just going to have to stay mindful of that and try to make progress on my own.

I feel like the work I've been doing in therapy has helped; we've talked through some difficult things that I hadn't dealt with. It's like I've shoved all this painful stuff into a cupboard, which burst open before Christmas during my breakdown.

I've spent the time in therapy sorting through the contents of the cupboard in an effort to clear out some of it. Eventually it'd be good to have cleared out all of it, or at least reached a point where I'm not scared of what's left.

Here's hoping!

H x

Day 59

I had my second session with the support worker today. We talked through some of the intrusive thoughts I had captured and tried to unpick some of the interlinked issues. It was all a bit underwhelming.

Apparently, I fall into a "grey area" between two levels of support, which is why we're struggling to align what the support worker does with what I need. Just for starters, there shouldn't be a grey area – when you define any scale or assessment criteria you always test it to ensure it is complete. Sorry, that's the Project Manager and Performance Analyst in me, but there really shouldn't be a grey area!

Whilst I'm content that the support worker is seeking advice and actually putting me back for re-assessment, things are frustratingly slow.

It also means that I view the time with the support worker as temporary, which means I'm not able to build the relationship with her that's needed for this to be effective. I feel unable to be completely open and vulnerable with her because it's likely I'm going to have to do it all again with someone else soon.

All in all, this is a very frustrating and ineffective process, which isn't benefitting any of the parties involved.

It's difficult to keep hope alive when this is what I'm experiencing. I really hope something changes pretty quickly!

H x

Day 60

I'm having trouble accepting that I will always feel this way. It won't always be as bad as this and I'll hopefully have a bigger toolbox to help me deal with it, but it'll always be there.

I'll always have to make sure I look after myself and pace myself if I'm tired or stressed to prevent it taking hold again. I know that just sounds sensible but I'm struggling to accept that I'm fallible, that I need to change.

Why can't I do everything? Why do I need to slow down? Why do I have to change?

It makes me feel weak, a failure, not enough.

My focus needs to be on changing my mindset, improving how I think about the changes to make them positive: I deserve to take care of myself, no one can do everything without taking care of themselves. It's only by luck that I've made it this far living the way I have.

I need to love myself enough to want to take care of me.

I'm starting that process with the affirmations, meditation and yoga. It's baby steps at the moment but I'm starting to feel more positive about it, which I hope is only the start.

Onward and upward!

H x

Affirmations

I have long thought I am 'broken', not just because I struggle with my mental health but because I can't get the hang of traditional mindfulness. Mindfulness is portrayed as something that anyone can do and that works for everyone, but

I just don't get on with it. I find it impossible to clear my mind and focus on each moment, even with a guided practice.

So, affirmations have been a real revelation for me. They're not something I've ever known much about or considered the power of, but WOW! I wish I'd discovered them earlier.

An affirmation can be anything that resonates with you and helps you focus on love rather than fear. I find them most helpful when they seek to address my fear statement or a particular state of mind or if they help me to focus on my vision.

Some of my favourite affirmations are:

I claim and honour my true voice
I am ready to go big, rise up and step into my power
I am enough, just as I am
Strength and courage flow through me

These were given to me by my yogi friend Alix over at Core Stories Yoga and you are welcome to use them or create your own.

When I first started using affirmations, I had them on Post-its everywhere, all over the house, my computer, my notebook. I also used to set alerts on my phone to remind me of my daily affirmation at hourly intervals throughout each day. I found that taking a couple of minutes to take some deep breaths and recite my affirmation to myself really helped to reconnect me. It makes me feel instantly calmer and helps to ward off unhelpful thoughts or images.

The latest affirmation I've added to my collection is:

Remember who you are

Whilst it's reminiscent of *The Lion King* (always a good thing in my book!), I love this one as it calls straight to my big dreams and vision of my best self. I use it often, particularly when I'm in a new or nerve-racking situation. These words help bring me strength, allow me to raise my head, smile and cope with whatever is happening.

I know now that the best version of me is confident, capable, open and welcoming. She can communicate well, build relationships and overcome challenges using creativity and with empathy for those around her.

'Remember who you are' allows me to access the best version of myself when fear is blocking my path.

You can do this too – pick an affirmation that calls to you and sit with it a while. Close your eyes, breathe deeply and let the words roll over you. Connect the words of the affirmation with how calm and clear you feel, allow yourself to visualise your best self, living your big dreams.

Dig deep and connect the words to your true self, your heart.

The more you practice this, the greater the impact. You will be able to use the affirmation to quickly calm yourself and call forward the strength you need to face whatever situation is arising.

Affirmation Exercise:

Work out what your fear statement is and then choose some words from the selection below (or feel free to choose others that resonate with you) and use these to create your own affirmations.

Chapter 6

Practice, Practice, Practice

As a good friend once told me: 'Practice is a choice, not a chore.' This little sentence changed my approach to recovery completely! I'd been stuck feeling frustrated that I *had* to do all these things and work to change my life in order to feel better when "other people don't have to". But that all changed with this sentence. I realised that yes, recovery is hard work and creating a life that I can thrive in will take time and effort. But it is a choice. I can choose to stay stuck and unhappy, living a life I don't enjoy and that doesn't serve me, or I can choose to do the work to change that. In all its frustrating, wiggly, effortful glory, this work will get me to where I want to be: living a life that fits me. The real me.

So, when you want to give up, ask yourself this: a year from now, will I wish that I had started this work today? One day, or day one – you decide.

Day 61

Today was such a lovely sunny day that I meditated outside this morning. It was a great way to start the day. I felt calm and energised, which made a very welcome change.

We took the children to the park and had a lovely time running about. It made me really happy to be able to actually enjoy some time with them. It's been so long that I was worried I'd lost the ability to have fun with my children.

It's really awful feeling like you don't enjoy time with your children. I feel guilty, ashamed and a bit broken to be honest. Today has given me hope that there will be more fun times to come.

As part of my therapy, I'm realising that I've spent my life feeling judged and trying to be everything to everyone so that people like me/don't leave me. Whilst we're slowly unpicking the details of that, I'm trying to identify things that are truly 'me'.

I'm thinking about the clothes I wear, activities I do – everything. It's hard to confront some of this stuff but I know I need to do it in order to start being more compassionate towards myself.

I am trying to look at this as a chance to connect with myself, to understand what truly makes me tick and find my voice again.

I'm worried about what people around me will think or say. I have always taken any comments as negative and tried to change that part of myself to please the commenter.

I don't want to do that anymore.

I want to be true to myself and sod everyone else!

H x

Day 62

Today I spent the day in a personal development workshop, the second of four day-long workshops focusing on who we are as leaders, our values and our goals. I usually really enjoy sessions like this but, at the moment, I'm finding them quite confronting and difficult.

I know that it's because I'm in a vulnerable place at the moment and actually that's a bit of a positive. The workshops are complementing the work I'm doing in therapy and, actually, because I am vulnerable I feel I'm more open to some of the ideas and changes being suggested.

I feel like a picture of who I truly am; personality, values, core beliefs and direction are just hovering slightly out of reach. At the moment, it's a haze of words, feelings and vague ideas, but I feel that this will get clearer and clearer as I do more work. One day I'll be able to see the whole picture clearly and then I can start to move forward.

It wasn't very long ago that I just felt completely lost and overwhelmed by it all. With no idea how to start, let alone a view of the finish line. In that sense I can see that I've come a long way and want to celebrate it! I know there is a long way left to go but, as I learnt today, I need to get comfortable with being uncomfortable.

This really resonated with me because I realise that a lot of my behaviours have been driven by a fear of being uncomfortable – from avoiding presentations at work, steering clear of situations that give me panic attacks to wearing certain clothes so that I 'fit in' – the spectrum is huge.

The work I'm doing at the moment is trying to get comfortable with myself so that my confidence increases, and I can stop the unhelpful behaviours and thinking patterns that are having a negative impact on me.

And, let's be honest, therapy is hugely uncomfortable and I'm doing a lot of that at the moment. By the end of this period in my life, I'll be so comfortable with being uncomfortable that I'll be unstoppable!

H x

Day 63

It's interesting what you learn when you start questioning your choices and decisions. I've recently learned that jeans really aren't my style, but they've been the main part of my wardrobe for most of my life!

I know that's not life-changing stuff, but it just goes to show the extent I've been hiding my true self.

I'm still working through what feels like layers of anxious thoughts and habits. If I can strip away some of those layers, then I might have the headspace to start moving forward.

It's no easy task, though. These beliefs are well ingrained and won't change at the flick of a switch. It's going to take me a while to understand why I believe that unless I look a certain way (which I never quite achieve) people will not accept/love me.

This is just one example, but working it through looks like this: it's about understanding what the 'certain way' actually looks like, breaking it down to understand why each component is important, understanding where the link to people not accepting/loving me comes from. Then I need to reframe each element to create a new, healthier belief, and practice that belief until it becomes habit and replaces the old one.

That's an awful lot of work to cover for each of my unhelpful beliefs, especially as I don't yet have professional help for this (it's not covered by the support worker).

Still, knowing what needs to happen and having an awareness of what to work on reframing is a really good start.

H x

Exercise

What are your unhelpful beliefs? How might you reframe them into something healthier? Use a journal or download the worksheet from my website (https://www.thementalhealthcommunity.co.uk/tools) to record your beliefs and work through reframing them.

Day 64

I think my next focus in my recovery needs to be my diet. I have a bad relationship with food and, when this breakdown all kicked off before Christmas, I was barely eating anything.

The medication I'm taking makes me feel really unwell if I don't eat, so I've been living off mainly toast, pasta and pizza for the last two months as I just can't face 'proper' food.

I didn't feel mentally supported and hadn't worked any of the issues through before I started taking the medication, so the poor eating habits haven't changed. It now feels like a huge task to work on my food issues so that I can eat properly again.

I'm worried because paying close attention to what I'm eating really doesn't work well for me. Plus, meal planning and prep takes extra energy spoons that I just don't have at the moment.

The sensible option seems to be to just carry on as I am and deal with the food stuff later. However, I know that's a false economy because of the impact food has on mental health.

I know that by eating better I will feel better and have more spoons to tackle other areas of my recovery. I guess I just need to pick a place and start!

It feels like such a huge task to think of healthier food options that are enticing enough to encourage me to eat but that don't take huge amounts of effort to make.

I need to break this down a bit: breakfast, lunch, dinner and snacks. I started making granola bars for breakfast, which are great, and the recipe makes a big batch that lasts me a couple of weeks.

So maybe I'll tackle lunch next. I'll start looking at ideas and see if I can find something that I fancy eating.

I feel this is a step in the right direction and if I just keep slowly working at it then, eventually, I'll have covered all meals and snacks!

H x

Day 65

Today I had a check-in with Occupational Health at work and a session with the solution-based therapist.

Both appointments helped me to see how far I've come in the last few months, which is a reminder I needed. It's so easy to get weighed down with how much further there is to go and how much work is left to do.

My solution-based therapist used a really good analogy to describe a recovery journey: recovery is like learning to drive – when you first start you have to work really hard to remember everything you're supposed to be practicing. But after lots of lessons and practice, all the things you have to do to stay well are so ingrained that you do them automatically.

This analogy has really helped me to deal with what feels like an overwhelming workload of tools and techniques that I am using many of my daily energy spoons to practice.

It's helpful to remind myself that eventually this will get easier and will feel more natural. I just need to keep putting the work in. Easier said than done when some days I can barely do the basics due to fatigue. On those days, I am working at being kind to myself, having breaks and trying to take it easy.

It's all a huge learning curve, but I've never been afraid of hard work, so I'm just doing what I can each day until it all gets easier.

H x

Day 66

I now feel a huge sense of achievement for even the most basic of things. Today I have done the food shopping, baked a birthday cake for my husband (cherry and marzipan cake – yum!) and cleaned the kitchen.

On a normal day that would be easy for me – nothing out of the ordinary. But at the moment it's a huge win! What I'm working on at the moment is celebrating these wins. It feels weird and unnatural at the moment, but I want it to be normal, I want to always celebrate the wins.

I thought I might celebrate my win by doing something creative. I've been struggling to find the inspiration and energy spoons to get making but I'm hoping I can use the spark from my win to get something started.

I've just bought a pattern to make myself a skirt and the other day I bought some new jewellery-making supplies. I'll get a few things out and see if inspiration hits.

It'd be great to get back into crafting again. It's such a positive and mindful activity, which I really enjoy. I just need to be careful I'm not falling into old habits and being overly critical of my work.

I need to remember that I am enough. That whatever I make is something to be proud of because I made it and enjoyed doing so.

H x

Day 67

A positive day again today. I am happy with the jewellery I made yesterday and wore it today. It's great to be creative again; this is the first time in ages that I've felt creative, so it's another sign of progress.

I am starting to visualise how I want my life to move forward now. For me, this is a great step because it wasn't that long ago that I couldn't see a future.

I'd love to create a future where I can exercise my creativity regularly, alongside all the other things that I'm discovering help to keep me well. Things like walking with a friend, pottering in the garden, yoga and meditation.

I'm just starting to allow rough plans for the future to take root so they can grow and hopefully steer me towards a plan. I need to be careful not to try and do everything at once. I don't want to overtake my recovery by having a few good days and trying to fix the world!

There's still so much I'm unsure of, so much to learn and practice that there's not much space for anything else. At the moment, recovery is a full-time job, but I'm keeping hope that it'll get easier and then I'll be able to focus more on plans for the future.

Right now, my future needs to be as small as the next few minutes, hours, days. But one day, hopefully not too far away, my future will stretch out ahead of me like an empty beach ready for me to explore.

H x

Day 68

Sunday crafting today. World Book Day is coming up, so I need to make a costume for my eldest. I've known this for a while but have been putting it off because it takes a lot of my energy spoons and I've been scared of ruining it.

After my happiness with the jewellery I made, I figured it was a good time to crack on with the costume. I went to my parents' house for moral support and spent the day drawing bones, cutting them out of felt and sewing them on to black trousers and a t-shirt.

It was draining but it's done now. He's really chuffed with it and it looks okay. I'm not embarrassed to send him to school in it, so I'm definitely counting it as a win!

It's achievements like this that I need to savour, to lock in my mind as evidence that I can do things, I am enough. It feels a bit silly to celebrate such small wins, but changing a long-held thought pattern is hard. It takes time and a lot of work to re-wire your brain. Celebrating all of these wins is a key part of that work.

It is only by consistently providing evidence for a new thought pattern that it will take root and become automatic. So, I'm consciously trying to celebrate all the wins, no matter how small.

I will change this, I am strong and I will succeed – my affirmation for the day!

H x

Day 69

I've felt really out of sorts today. Right before waking up I had a really vivid, unhappy dream and so I've felt a bit bereft all day. Even though I've had plenty to focus on, it's been difficult to shift this feeling.

The dreams that I remember are always quite detailed and specific. They are never happy dreams. I usually spend the following day battling to regain a sense of peace whilst I try to make sense of the dream and how it makes me feel.

Today I've tried to be kinder to myself. I've allowed myself to feel whatever I needed to as I process the dream and things it stirred up for me. I've really used my affirmation as a reminder to be compassionate towards myself too – I choose loving thoughts today.

I am working to accept that sometimes I need to have low power days; days where stuff still gets done but at a slower speed and I'm careful about not choosing tasks that are overly challenging.

Today was one of those days and it actually worked well. I achieved more than I thought I would but don't feel battered by the day. I feel this is a hugely positive step for me. Usually, I'd have been pushing myself all day and berating myself for not doing enough. I would have ended the day feeling awful and hating my failure.

But not today.

Today I accept myself and celebrate that I'm able to have compassion enough to have a low power day. I choose loving thoughts today.

H x

Day 70

It's tentative but I think there is a bit of movement in the right direction in terms of support. My support worker called to postpone our appointment this week. Whilst that's not great, it's for a positive reason.

The support worker put my case back for reassessment and it's been decided that I will meet with a psychiatrist. The support worker wasn't clear on the details other than this would be for "advice". But I hope that the outcome of the appointment will lead to more appropriate support/treatment.

I'm so lucky to have such a great support network. People who keep me strong enough to stand up for myself. Otherwise, I don't think I'd have made it this far. It's so frustrating and difficult to have to fight just to get the support I need.

At least work have been able to support me with access to therapy in the meantime. I feel a bit lost now that my sessions with the solution-based therapist are over. I can go back and pay to have private therapy with her but the rules state that there needs to be a gap of three months before I can do this.

I understand that this rule is there to protect vulnerable people being pushed to pay for therapy, but three months is a long time when you're still fragile.

All I can keep doing is practice what I've learnt and keep plugging away at trying to deal with life.

Fingers crossed for more positive therapy news soon!

H x

Day 71

Today is a milestone for me. Today was the first time I've said it out loud: I had a breakdown. It's taken me this long to understand and accept that's what happened and for me this is a milestone to be celebrated.

I celebrate that I am able to be open about what's happening and be truly honest about what I'm going through. I see this as a great milestone in my recovery and a really positive step towards a healthier future.

Of course, it won't feel like that for some people. I accept (although I heartily disagree) that there is still a stigma attached to this. But I am willing to stand up and fight against it.

I'm also aware that in being so open about my struggles and recovery journey I may upset people I care about. This affects me hugely and I feel enormous guilt, responsibility and sadness about it.

I really hope that I don't cause hurt to the people I care about, that certainly isn't my intention. However, I need this openness and acceptance of the truth of all this in order to heal.

If I continue to hide it, or play down the severity of how I feel, then I will fall back into unhealthy thought and behaviour patterns and the cycle will begin again.

So, let me say this: I'm sorry. I'm sorry for putting you through this and for how my words might make you feel. Please don't feel sorry for me, just continue to support me and share in my celebration of successes, however small they may be.

I love you.

H x

Day 72

I woke up today feeling lethargic and struggling to get going. My body ached and my brain was foggy. I felt so rubbish that I almost cancelled the walk I had arranged with a friend, especially when I saw it was raining.

I'm so glad I didn't cancel, though. After an hour's wet and very blustery walk along the canal with a good friend to chat to I felt much better. Even though I was cold and wet, my brain felt clearer and I was able to head home and get some work done.

Today was always going to be a low power day as I had a busy day of meetings in the office yesterday. I was worried that I wouldn't even manage low power, but the walk really sorted me out.

I'd like to get to a point where even walking by myself helps. At the moment, when I'm alone, particularly if I'm feeling tired, my thoughts easily spiral out of control. This allows the intrusive thoughts to take hold and right now I need to do my best to avoid that.

Today was rescued by a walk and, now that the children are in bed, I'm going to have a restful evening with a book. Hopefully this'll help me recharge so that I wake up tomorrow with a full set of energy spoons to see me through.

H x

Day 73

I've really struggled today. I feel groggy, grumpy and I'm losing the battle with my thoughts. It's only this afternoon that I've realised it's been two days since I spent a day in the office. It seems to be the pattern that it takes me two days to recover from a high power day, with the second day being the worst.

Now I've remembered that, I'm finding it easier to accept my feelings and be kind to myself. I've had a hot shower and practiced some yoga whilst reciting my mantra (in my head).

This is really helping to clear my thoughts to make way for love and compassion.

I just wish that it didn't take me two days to recover! I know I need to take things slowly and give myself time, but sometimes that's just so frustrating. I just need to keep practicing the things that help and making time for myself.

I'm still pretty bad at making time for myself and taking time to practice or do therapy exercises. I just feel so guilty about it. I don't really know how to change that other than just keep doing it.

I guess it will get easier in time. I'll get more used to asserting the new boundaries and everyone around me will come to expect it too.

I do wish that recovery had a fast-forward button though!

H x

Day 74

After battling with a cold the last few days, it's finally taken over. My body aches, my head is so foggy it hurts and I'm just feeling a bit sorry for myself.

I hadn't considered the impact that getting ill might have on my recovery. Even something as minor as a cold has affected my ability to practice yoga, meditation and affirmations. I'm struggling to do anything more taxing than sitting on the sofa!

I don't usually struggle with colds, they come and go without much impact on my daily life. So, it's a surprise that I'm suffering so much, but I guess that's because I'm already low.

I'm finding it difficult to be kind to myself; after all, it is just a cold. But I recognise that this is really unhelpful, so I am trying to give myself a break.

I'm trying to talk kindly to myself and congratulate myself for doing things that just feel too difficult today. This has helped me make dinner for the family and do some laundry. I even managed a quick trip to the shop.

I'm definitely celebrating that one – I find supermarkets a huge sensory overload at the moment. They usually trigger panic attacks or intrusive thoughts, which I then struggle to recover from.

But I did it! Even when I'm feeling so low, I can push myself further than I expect.

That's definitely something to celebrate.

H x

Day 75

It's fair to say I've hit a bit of a bump in my recovery. I feel stuck in my own head, bombarded with unwelcome thoughts and images, none of which are from a place of love.

I can't seem to stop hating on myself for feeling this way. My mind keeps telling me what a failure I am because even if I can force myself to practice my tools for recovery they aren't helping right now.

I'm not exercising or even going outside unless I'm forced to. I am still eating rubbish and am struggling to even do the basics to look after myself.

I just don't have the energy or the drive to get up and get on with it. It all just feels too much, too hard and I can't do it. I feel like such a waste of space.

I'm not sure how to turn this around. I have spent the last couple of days waiting to feel better. Every time I go to bed, I have hope that I'll wake up feeling different. Clearly, it's going to take more than a good night's sleep.

I'm going to have to dig deep, get up and push myself to work harder on my recovery. Practice more, get dressed and go out, cook proper food.

Ugh. I'm not sure I can face it.

Where am I going to find the energy and motivation to do all of that?

Hopefully the universe will send me some!

H x

Day 76

It's really easy when you hit a 'bump' in the recovery road to lose sight of all the progress you've made and feel like you're back at square one again.

It's also really easy to slip straight back into old, unhealthy thinking patterns and behaviours.

What I need to work hard to remember is that I have come such a long way and have more tools and awareness now than I've ever had. Yes, there's a long way still to go. But the climb back up when I hit a bump doesn't need to be so high.

I can take a couple of steps back and still be in a better place than I was a few months ago. I don't need to feel like my world is crumbling again or that I'm helpless.

It's totally okay to take a few days to rest, regroup and refocus. I can start to have faith in my practice and know that I will get back up again.

It's really positive that I can start to see the time between bumps lengthening... it was only a matter of weeks ago that I was still in a huge hole that felt permanent.

It's also positive that I can acknowledge that, even whilst I'm actually feeling stuck. I'm going to celebrate that as a win and hope that it sparks enough lift to get me over this bump in the road.

H x

Day 77

Tough day today – my anxiety and intrusive thoughts

have been really high all day. I've not been able to see above them to work with my affirmation or meditation. This is where some professional help would really be beneficial.

I'm utterly exhausted, but too scared to go to bed in case the night is bad, and I don't feel better tomorrow.

I went out to catch up with my best friend last night. I've been pretty rubbish at staying in touch with my friends, so it was good to see her. Trouble is, I got home late and was so exhausted that I forgot to take my medication. I've only just realised, and I wonder how much of an impact that is having on how I feel today.

I need to try and set myself up for having a better day tomorrow, but don't have the energy to even think about what I need to do.

I really wish I could just get out of my own head and do something useful. I have no energy spoons left and I can't stop being cross with myself.

Today is a tough day. I have to hope that tomorrow will feel better. I'm scared of falling back to where I was.

I wish there was a professional I could call.

H x

NB: If you're feeling like this and want someone to talk to, the people listed at the back of this book (p126) can help.

Day 78

Today I've tried to spend the day focusing on the three Rs: Rest, Regroup, Refocus.

I started the day setting out my time so that I had clear space for work and for each of the three Rs. I made sure to allow time to be productive with work tasks followed by a period of rest.

I took time to listen to a couple of inspiring talks to help me regroup. I find it really helpful to listen to other people's journeys. It helps me to pull myself out of a funk and regroup ready for moving forward.

I spent longer than usual meditating, followed by a good restorative yoga practice. I really find this helps me to refocus on myself and my recovery, but I struggle to do that if I haven't taken the time to rest and regroup first.

Today has helped me pull myself out of the dip I've been in for the last few days. I still have some work to do, though, because my first thought when getting ready for ballet was that I look awful!

Baby steps…

H x

Day 79

I've been in the office all day today. It was mostly back-to-back meetings, so I am now completely wiped out.

I feel so drained, I honestly feel like I might collapse. I thought things might be easier by now, I hoped it would be better.

I feel so defeated.

My body aches, my head is fuzzy, I can't think straight and I'm on the verge of tears.

I don't know how to make this easier.

I need some help.

H x

Day 80

Why is everything so much harder when you feel down? Everyday things like cooking, showering and even just brushing my teeth feel like a mountain to climb on days like this.

It just adds to my intrusive thoughts convincing me that I'm a waste of space. It's days like today that it takes everything I've got to get out of bed instead of curling up under the duvet to hide.

I'm trying really hard to be kind to myself, to remember my affirmation and have faith that this is just a blip. It's just so bloody difficult to constantly battle my brain when I'm so exhausted.

We have a busy weekend filled with lovely things ahead but, honestly, I can't even bear to think about it.

I desperately want to look forward to things again. I thought I was getting there but this last week has been really tough.

Turns out I'm not doing well without therapy!

Fingers crossed for a better day tomorrow.

H x

Day 81

I finally had a decent sleep last night – enough hours plus no vivid, awful dreams that wake me up. Good sleep really is fundamental if I want any chance of getting through the next day.

There's lots to do this weekend and I've been struggling to keep calm! I've reverted to making lists to try and free up space in my head.

It sounds really silly, but writing a list really does help. Even if the list is huge and daunting, I feel instantly calmer seeing it written down rather than fighting for space in my head.

I feel a bit like I'm tackling a major event at the moment – I have lists for a number of things and I'm focusing on just working my way through. One step at a time, not looking further than a couple of steps ahead so that I don't get overwhelmed.

I feel sad that I can't look out further and be excited about things to come, or even enjoy the journey. But I have hope that I'll be able to do that again soon. One thing at a time and eventually I'll be out of this bit and on to something better.

Affirmation of the day: strength and courage flows through me.

H x

Day 82

It's been a busy weekend, but as I sit here with a cuppa on Sunday evening, I feel content. Tired, but content. We've done everything we needed to and had some fun along the way, so I'm counting that as a win.

It's wonderful to be able to not only survive a busy weekend but actually enjoy parts of it too. A definite sign of progress.

I expect I'll be exhausted for the next few days but I'm setting the intention now that I'll be kind to myself. I plan to choose an affirmation each day and try to get some exercise a few times this week.

I know that I've struggled recently and there were a few points where I was sure I'd slip back into complete darkness. But I worked hard to keep my focus and hopefully that's paying off.

It's difficult to stay hopeful when the darkness starts creeping in. I instinctively try to hold on; grip fiercely to my current 'normal' for fear it will slip away.

I think it might actually help me if I learn to ride the wave a bit. To let go, ease off and see what I learn on the journey. As long as I keep hold of my practice, I can stay hopeful that I'll come out of the other side relatively unscathed.

H x

Day 83

I feel like I've hit a wall with my recovery. I can get myself through most days and tasks (school pick up, shopping, etc.). I still find them difficult and need to actively manage myself through them, but I can do it. I'm still working on eating and socialising – I knew these would be things that might take me longer, but I can see progress here too.

However, I don't seem to be able to move forward. I'm struggling to expand my successes so far or build up to new things. I'm finding it really frustrating.

I'm really feeling the lack of professional help now – it's affecting my recovery and I'm worried that if nothing happens soon, I'll be stuck in this tiny existence for ages.

It really does feel like I'm living a very tiny life right now. The list of things I can do or eat and people I can see is small. I have big dreams and ideas, but the reality is too much for me at the moment.

I know I need to be patient and that things will improve with time, but I know that there's still so much to be resolved and I need professional help to do that.

It's not easy being patient when I've been waiting so long for care, which should have been available so quickly given how severely ill I've been.

I just need to trust that the universe has a plan and let it happen.

H x

Day 84

Today I have felt energised by discussing ideas for the future with a friend. It's been really great to spark ideas off each other and feel excited about the possibility of a new future.

It's difficult to maintain that feeling when I'm alone, though. The thoughts creep in telling me it'll never happen,

I'm not enough to make it work, there's no way I can have a future like this.

I'm trying to manage the thoughts with my affirmation of the day: I am enough just as I am. But it's tricky to resist spiralling through the bad thoughts and talking myself out of the ideas.

I've got a session with my coach this week. I'm hoping to talk some of this through and maybe start turning it into plans. I think practical steps towards achieving goals will help me to feel more optimistic and grounded in my plans for my future.

I really enjoy talking with my coach. Not only is she completely lovely, she also really helps to alter my perspective. I usually start our sessions with 'I want to do all these things but…' and she talks me through everything, gently challenging me to find solutions and eliminate barriers.

I always leave our sessions feeling inspired and ready to start achieving whatever goals I've set. I wish I could bottle the feeling so I can tap into it when my motivation is hard to find!

H x

REFOCUS – the final step

Once I've rested and regrouped, I then feel able to refocus on myself, on my recovery or moving towards the life I want to lead.

It's in this space that I can see more clearly the

direction I want to take and the hurdles standing in my way. It's only by creating this space for yourself to refocus on you that you can start to undo the old habits driven by fear and make new habits forged by love.

Allow yourself to open up, be vulnerable, be honest with yourself about your dreams, about the life you want to lead. This feels awkward and unnatural at first, but trust me it's worth it.

This journey (I hate that word, but there isn't a better one to describe this!) has taught me so much about myself that I was afraid to acknowledge. I buried parts of myself because of fear of judgement, fear of not being enough. This whole experience has opened me up to who I truly am inside and has helped me to welcome that self into being. It's not easy; fear creeps in without me realising and I slip back into old habits and unhelpful behaviours. But by stepping through the three Rs, I can bring myself back to a place of acceptance and love.

When you're in this period of refocus, take every opportunity to write goals and action steps; the more detailed and clearer the better. I make endless lists both on paper and in an app that feel huge and daunting, but they help me to stay on track even on days when I'm feeling a bit wobbly.

Usually when I'm refocusing, my goals or dreams feel really tangible and almost real; this is a really key time for me to take action, before the darkness creeps in or imposter syndrome starts chipping away at my vision.

For me, this usually involves writing goals and action lists; a step-by-step to achieving each small part of my vision and then completing some of those actions. You can do this however feels right for you; make a vision board, take some photographs, make a vlog of yourself talking things through, draw a series of pictures… the possibilities are almost endless. The key is to go with what feels natural for you. What's important is the content; you're capturing your goals and actions so they can start to form a plan, a framework for you to achieve your goals.

This can serve as a prompt or reference for you to follow. It can give structure to your journey that you can continue to refer to and make progress against, even when you can't see the end goal clearly.

You might struggle with this, there will inevitably be false starts and hiccups along the way, but if you keep practicing it'll come, I promise.

Here's a visualisation exercise that helps me refocus on my vision for the future. You can use this prompt or there's an audio version where I talk you through it on my website (https://www.thementalhealthcommunity.co.uk/tools). Grab a pen and paper to use at the end.

Exercise

Close your eyes and focus on your breathing, feel your breath as it travels into your body, filling your lungs and relaxing your belly.

Breathe out fully in one push through your mouth.

Now repeat the inhalation whilst you picture a ball of light at your core. This light is your energy, your power. Notice what colour it is, how strong it is.

As you breathe in, the light grows and gets brighter, then as you slowly exhale, focus on pushing the light around your body until everywhere is lit up and pulsing with the energy of your power.

As you continue to feed your power with your breath, really focus on how it makes you feel; is it a calm energy that helps restore and heal you until you are whole again, or is it a jolt of lightning that powers you up so you feel you can set the world on fire? Or something different… whatever manifests for you, hold that feeling as you open your heart up and let your dreams and vision for your future flow.

Step into your vision, what does it look like? How does it feel? Who are you here, what are you doing?

Take a minute to revel in your vision, feel how it is to really live it.

Now as you come back to the room, I want you to bring that feeling with you and say to yourself: I am ready to go big, rise up and step into my power. I am ready to go big, rise up and step into my power.

Just spend a couple of minutes writing or drawing what you've just seen and felt. Try not to think too hard – just put your pen on the paper and let it flow.

Read over what you've just written, what's one step, however tiny, that you can take now towards making this a reality? See if you can write a few steps towards achieving your vision and maybe add a date to turn them into actions that you can achieve in a realistic timescale.

Repeat this exercise whenever you need to open your heart and connect with your vision.

Chapter 7

Progress

In this chapter you'll see that because the work was paying off and I was starting to feel better, I pushed myself more. As a consequence, I needed to refocus on looking after myself, taking downtime and planning in quieter days.

It's great to be able to tap into the life you want to lead. To tackle things that have previously felt out of reach and succeed – what a feeling! Celebrate the progress you're making. Look at how far you've come and the work you've done to get here and congratulate yourself for being so bloody awesome! Then rest, take it easy and draw your focus inwards to build on that feeling for tomorrow.

Day 85

Today has been exhausting. I had to present the work I've been doing to our governing body for approval. I find presentations difficult at the best of times, but now more than ever I feel the pressure, I think because work has been a focus for me. Through all the darkness of a breakdown, work was my focus. No matter how I felt, I was focused on work and delivering my project. I felt that work was the anchor preventing me from spiralling away and getting lost in the darkness.

Whilst that did serve a purpose, I now have a lot of myself invested in the project and so it feels personal. I am passionate about the project and believe in what I am delivering. I know it would be healthier if I could separate myself from work a bit. But then I think it wouldn't have the same ability to anchor me.

I am trying to embrace my emotional tie to my work and use it to my advantage in winning the hearts and minds of the people the project has had an impact on. That means I need to accept that days like today will be tough and feel personal. Luckily, I have a great team around me at work, they support me and are fantastic cheerleaders for the project.

We got approval today, which is such great validation for what we're doing. Now the hard work of delivery starts!

H x

Day 86

I definitely had a low power day today, but I managed to do what I needed to at work and went for a walk with some good friends.

When I'm exhausted, getting out in the fresh air can give me the lift I need to get through the day. Even if it is really difficult to get myself out of the door.

I find it so helpful to talk things through with a

supportive friend. It helps me to order my thoughts, breaks up unhelpful thinking patterns and gives me an opportunity to see things from a different perspective.

Taking the time to get out, especially when coupled with talking to friends, really helps to lift my mood. I came back feeling energised and focused, ready to tackle the rest of my working day.

Making the time to do something restorative like a walk always pays off for me in improved mindset and productivity. I still feel guilty for taking the time, but I'm learning to respond to that with a reminder of the benefits. Every time I make time for myself it gets a little bit easier, so I know it'll be part of my 'normal' in the future.

I have hope that self-care activities will eventually be easier for me to take the time for, without guilt or bad feeling. I look forward to it!

H x

Day 87

Today could easily have gone horribly wrong. I had a late night and, added to my week of high energy activities, I woke up feeling lethargic.

Today is the day I spend at home with my daughter. She's loving, funny and so kind. She's also four and that comes with tantrums, boundary pushing and strongly exerting her ideas. So, when I'm tired, I know there's potential for us to clash.

I really didn't want that today. So, I spoke with her and

explained that I was tired but wanted us to have a good day. By taking the time to talk about what we were going to do and things we needed to get done, we were able to make a plan for the day that we were both happy with.

It would have been easier not to try and have that talk, to sit us both in front of the television for the day. To be honest, there are days I do that and that's totally okay. But I didn't want that for today.

As a result, today has been a really positive day – we've achieved a lot and haven't really clashed.

I really feel that being open and honest about how I felt and being flexible about the day is something I can apply to help myself. Even on days where it's just me, I can flex the day to fit how I'm feeling. This will really help me to be kinder to myself and knock some of that harsh self-talk on the head.

I claim and honour my true voice.

H x

Day 88

There are days when you think you're doing okay and then there are days like today that smack you in the face.

Today started off okay, but a throwaway comment triggered my brain into overdrive. I've spent the rest of the day trying desperately to slow my racing thoughts to a speed where I can manage them.

Each time I succeed, it's followed a few minutes later with a fresh wave of complete terror in only the way anxiety can deliver.

I breathe in courage and breathe out fear – my affirmation for today.

Tomorrow is another day.

H x

Day 89

It's been a gorgeous, sunny day today and as a result everyone has been in a good mood.

The children played outside on their bikes and with bubbles whilst I did some more work on our garden renovations. Keeping busy is a good way for me to keep my thoughts in check, especially if I'm struggling a bit.

I'm still trying to calm the rush of intrusive thoughts that started yesterday. It's really difficult to do, but I know I need to confront them in order to move on.

All my life, my coping mechanisms have been avoidance-based and it's really difficult to change that habit. It's only on days where I'm feeling safe and strong enough that I'm able to do this. I find it frustrating that it's so difficult for me to do, but I know it'll get easier with practice.

I'm feeling physically tired after my afternoon of digging. This is a nice change from my usual mental exhaustion. I'm conscious that I need to move my body more in order to improve both my physical and mental health.

I often find that some form of exercise, be that walking, gardening or a class, can help me to process unwelcome thoughts. Usually this is due to the mindful elements of focusing entirely on the present, on what my body is doing.

I just need to get the balance right – too much mental exhaustion means I can't make myself exercise.

I'm working on it.

H x

Day 90

I really struggled to face the day this morning, but I pushed through and got myself to the development workshop I was booked on.

I'm really glad I did. Today's workshop was about assertiveness and I know that's a key area of development for me.

We had some great conversations about our goals and the hurdles in our path to achieving them. I was anxious about sharing my vision for the future, but I'm so pleased I did.

My group were really supportive and gave me some great advice and feedback. This afternoon we had an opportunity to practice having assertive conversations and gave each other feedback to help us improve.

Today has been exhausting, but I have learnt a lot. I have a pretty clear vision for my future that I want to build, which is definitely going to require me to be assertive!

I'm going to keep practicing what I've learnt today and that includes sharing my vision for the future, starting now.

I want to use my experience to support others who

are struggling. I also want to use my experience to inform improvements in mental health provision. I've got a few ideas for how I might go about this, which I'll write about soon.

I claim and honour my true voice.

H x

Day 91

Today we had a 'department day' where we all got together to celebrate our successes and talk about the next steps for our team.

To be honest I was dreading it. I've not seen many people in the department for a few months as I've been mostly working from home, popping in for meetings when I need to.

I've certainly not spoken to any of them about what I've been going through. So today was hard, not only because it's a whole day of having to hold myself together and be 'on it', but also because there would be the inevitable questions about where I'd been.

The good news is: I got through it!

I even managed to be open with a couple of people on a one-to-one basis. I made the decision this morning that if anyone asked me about where I'd been that I would be open and honest.

It's a difficult decision when you don't know what the reaction will be, but it's really important to me that I don't pretend anymore.

The people I shared with today were supportive and kind, which helps me have confidence to share again in the future. Being vulnerable is not something any of us really relish, but actually I believe it offers the biggest opportunities for connection and growth.

I have definitely planned in a quiet day to recover tomorrow!

H x

Day 92

Today has been a really interesting mix. I started off feeling very lethargic with little motivation for anything.

I had a lot to do following two days out of the office, so I got stuck in, albeit a little slowly! It was really difficult at first, but I had a couple of calls, which really piqued my enthusiasm and after those I was more able to crack on with tasks.

It's ended up being quite a productive day, which I really didn't expect!

It's amazing how simple things can make or break a day. What I'm learning is that I need to build a toolkit to rescue a day that's not going so well.

For me that's usually going for a walk, seeing a friend, taking time out to watch a television programme or to meditate.

It's good to learn that speaking to someone about something I find interesting or feel passionately about can also work. Especially as I spend a lot of time hiding from my phone at the moment!

Definitely something to add to my toolkit.

H x

Day 93

The week has really caught up with me today. I feel shattered, emotional and my body hurts.

I am struggling to make my brain work, despite desperately needing to prepare for a huge presentation next week.

But, worst of all, I have nothing left to share with my children. I have no patience for their usual shenanigans and can't even play with them. It's this that makes me feel truly awful.

The light within me has faded to a tiny flicker, just when I need it to be burning brightly.

H x

Day 94

Yep – I've definitely pushed myself too far this week. I am feeling pretty rotten inside and out, so I definitely need to take some time to recover this weekend.

I'm trying hard to be kind to myself and not get frustrated at all the things I can't do. It's difficult, though, and I feel like I need to do more to help myself.

I've been out in the fresh air and sunshine today and my parents came over to play with my youngest so I could rest a bit, which was a huge help.

I'm going to have a hot shower, meditate and then have an early night once the children are in bed.

Tomorrow is another day.

H x

Day 95

Although I have still felt exhausted today and have struggled with all that comes with the exhaustion, my thoughts have been lighter.

I have realised that over the last couple of weeks my boundaries have become a bit wonky again. I am giving work everything I have without keeping anything back for my recovery work or my family.

Now that I can see this, I can do something to shift the boundaries back again. I know that I have a ridiculously busy week at work this week, but I am determined to set time aside for me.

I can see a few small pockets of time between meetings and presentations, so I will timebox them for recovery. I'm not going to feel motivated to think about my affirmations on a day-by-day basis, so I'm going to select a few and programme them into my phone now so that they pop up regularly each day.

I've also booked out a couple of days the following week so that I have no meetings and can just have low-power days.

All the old feelings of guilt and unworthiness are creeping back in as I make these plans. But I know I need to be strong and carve out the time I need. Otherwise, I'm going to keep slipping backwards.

H x

Day 96

I'm really struggling to perceive myself from a place of love. I feel like I've gone back a few steps from the positive place I'd reached and now fear has taken over again.

I need to carve out some time for the three Rs this week – Rest, Regroup and Refocus. This needs to be my priority rather than work or all the other things to do.

I am my priority.

I want to have enough love for myself that I remove the barriers to me looking after myself.

I need to believe that I am worthy of this love, that I am enough.

I'm going to sit down and make a plan for the week to prioritise my care and help me get back to a place of love.

I am worthy of love and compassion.

I am enough.

H x

Day 97

I'm working hard to remind myself of how far I've come in my recovery. Of all the work I've done to shift my perspective from fear to love. Of the affirmations that are my lifeline each day and of my ongoing cycle of recovery: rest, regroup, refocus.

It's the constant awareness of my mindset, the addition to my mental load that I find exhausting. I push against having to do the work, wishing for an easier time of it. But I know that the work is essential if I want to recover and have a sustainable version of my best self.

It's that knowledge that keeps me going. It's definitely a marathon rather than a sprint, but I know I am continuing to make progress.

Recovery isn't linear. There are times I feel like I'm falling backwards rather than moving forwards. I'm learning to accept that this is part of the journey and is the universe's way of reminding me to take it steady and continue with my practice.

For me, recovery is about balance. It's about doing the hard work and balancing it out by finding things that bring me joy. Balancing the activity to move me forward with rest to help me get stronger. It's about rebuilding my life with better balance in the hope that this doesn't keep happening.

I choose loving thoughts today.

H x

Day 98

Today at work I stood up in front of a room of senior people and presented the work we've been doing in the project. It was a HUGE achievement for me, especially when there are days I still struggle to leave the house.

I've been really stressing about it (obviously!) and this morning I was shaking and actually thought I might faint at one point! But I did it! I had some really positive feedback and some useful conversations afterwards, which I'll follow up later.

For me, it's a testament to my inner strength and sheer determination that I managed to do this. I know the people in the audience will have no idea of the struggles I've been working through. They will also have no idea how reassuring their feedback is and how I'm using it to calm my inner critic who is intent on picking apart my performance.

Today has taken everything I've got. I feel like I could go to bed for a week now, but I'm so pleased I did it.

I'm pleased because I was convinced that I couldn't do it. I'm also pleased because I want to share my recovery story. I want to use it to talk to health services to help them improve and I want to help others on their own recovery path, but I can only do these things if I can talk in front of large groups.

Now I know I CAN do it.

H x

Day 99·

I've been thinking more about the things I've gained from the experience of having a breakdown and rebuilding myself. It's been a period of intense learning and reflection. I've reassessed what I do, how I behave, who I am.

It feels pretty self-absorbed, to be honest, but it is essential work if I want to get better. It's also ongoing. I'm continually talking myself through exercises to help me stay focused, exercises to try and bolster my almost non-existent resilience or to help me accept myself, love myself.

I've practised new techniques, grown my knowledge of theories, methods and practices aimed at personal development and my illness. I've also gained a different perspective about what's important to me and can use this to have greater understanding of other people's views and ideas. This is something that I use on a daily basis at work and home and I'll continue to try and grow this skill.

Whilst I wouldn't wish this experience on anyone, I have tried to bring some positives from the darkness. This is something I definitely want to continue, particularly if I can use my experience to help others. I'm working on a few ideas for this, but if you have any ideas, I'd love to hear them!

H x

Day 100

WOW. When I started writing, I never thought I'd manage to write every day for 100 days, but I DID IT!

Spending time each day writing, ordering my thoughts and reflecting on my day has helped bring me clarity, understanding and perspective. These things have really seen me through my rollercoaster ride of recovering from a breakdown.

Progress

I know I'm not recovered yet (if there even is a final state of 'recovered'); there are still issues I need to work through (I'm on a waiting list for therapy), resilience I need to build and energy I need to find. But I'm getting there, with baby steps I am learning how to have love and compassion for myself. I'm learning about what works for me in terms of therapy and relaxation techniques and I'm learning to open up, be vulnerable and accept that I'm not invincible.

My name is Hannah and I had a breakdown. I have a diagnosis of F41 Other Anxiety Disorders, which is severe and chronic. I love writing, reading, yoga, dancing and being outside. I don't like traditional mindfulness, wearing jeans, wasting time or therapies where I am required to fill out endless worksheets. I am learning to love rather than fear and I use affirmations to keep me in touch with that.

I'm going to keep writing about my journey and what I'm learning and will be sharing more soon.

Thank you for all your love, support and kind words, they have really kept me going.

H x

Epilogue

It's difficult to know how to end this book. I'd love to tell you that I've 'fixed' my mental health and never struggle with it. But the truth is mental health doesn't work like that. I have bad days and even bad weeks, it's just that now I have more understanding of my triggers and the tools that work for me. I can tell when I've been overdoing things, or not practising my wellness necessities and I know what to do to rectify it. I know when I can push myself and when to ease off and I'm much better at being able to assert my boundaries or ask for help.

I wish I had a magic wand to wave away all the darkness and noise in your head. I know from personal experience that there are times you wish you could scoop out your brain and wash away all the clouds. I've written this book to share with you the tools that worked for me and what makes them so effective is that they are built by you, with information you already have, put into a formula that consistently works.

I want you to know that however hopeless everything feels at the moment, you can do this. You can keep going and you CAN get to a place of balance where you feel in control and able to manage your mental health. You are never alone in this, right? And if you feel like you are then please, please reach out: to your friends and family, GP, local mental health services or to any of the organisations listed here. We all want to help you because we care about you and value you. You are worth helping.

It doesn't always have to feel dark and overwhelming. Start small and use the tools in this book to build your own framework for recovery and staying well. You've got this.

I hope my journey has brought you comfort, hope and inspiration for your own journey. If you want to let me know how you're doing, connect with other like-minded people or just say hi, please pop over to Instagram @ themhcommunity or Twitter @themh_community, I'd love to hear from you.

Remember, practice is a choice, not a chore.

Lots of love,

H x

People to contact for support:

1. Your GP
2. The Mental Health Community: www.thementalhealthcommunity.co.uk (this one is my charity working in local communities to support people struggling with their mental health)
3. The Samaritans: 116 123
4. Mind: https://www.mind.org.uk/information-support/ Or your local Mind branch
5. Shout: text SHOUT to 85258
6. More support organisations can be found on the NHS website: https://www.nhs.uk/conditions/stress-anxietydepression/mental-health-helplines/

Printed in Great Britain
by Amazon